A NOVEL BASED ON THE LIFE OF

MOTHER FRANCES X. CABRINI

GOD'S MESSENGER

THE ASTOUNDING ACHIEVEMENTS OF

MOTHER CABRINI

Nicole Gregory

THE **M**
MENTORIS
PROJECT

God's Messenger is a work of fiction. Some incidents, dialogue, and characters are products of the author's imagination and are not to be construed as real. Where real-life historical figures appear, the situations, incidents, and dialogue concerning those persons are based on or inspired by actual events. In all other respects, any resemblance to actual persons, living or dead, events, or locales is entirely coincidental.

The Mentoris Project
Barbera Foundation, Inc.
P.O. Box 1019
Temple City, CA 91780

Copyright © 2017 Barbera Foundation, Inc.
Cover photo: Courtesy of The Cabriniana Collection, Cabrini University, Radnor, PA
Cover design: Suzanne Turpin

More information at www.mentorisproject.org

ISBN: 978-1-947431-02-7

Library of Congress Control Number: 2017960064

All net proceeds from the sale of this book will be donated to Barbera Foundation, Inc. whose mission is to support educational initiatives that foster an appreciation of history and culture to encourage and inspire young people to create a stronger future.

The Mentoris Project is a series of novels and biographies about the lives of great men and women who have changed history through their contributions as scientists, inventors, explorers, thinkers, and creators. The Barbera Foundation sponsors this series in the hope that, like a mentor, each book will inspire the reader to discover how she or he can make a positive contribution to society.

Contents

Foreword

First and foremost, Mentor was a person. We tend to think of the word *mentor* as a noun (a mentor) or a verb (to mentor), but there is a very human dimension embedded in the term. Mentor appears in Homer's *Odyssey* as the old friend entrusted to care for Odysseus's household and his son Telemachus during the Trojan War. When years pass and Telemachus sets out to search for his missing father, the goddess Athena assumes the form of Mentor to accompany him. The human being welcomes a human form for counsel. From its very origins, becoming a mentor is a transcendent act; it carries with it something of the holy.

The Mentoris Project sets out on an Athena-like mission: We hope the books that form this series will be an inspiration to all those who are seekers, to those of the twenty-first century who are on their own odysseys, trying to find enduring principles that will guide them to a spiritual home. The stories that comprise the series are all deeply human. These books dramatize the lives of great men and women whose stories bridge the ancient and the modern, taking many forms, just as Athena did, but always holding up a light for those living today.

Whether in novel form or traditional biography, these books plumb the individual characters of our heroes' journeys. The power of storytelling has always been to envelop the reader in a vivid and continuous dream, and to forge a link with the subject. Our goal is for that link to guide the reader home with a new inspiration.

What is a mentor? A guide, a moral compass, an inspiration. A friend who points you toward true north. We hope that the Mentoris Project will become that friend, and it will help us all transcend our daily lives with something that can only be called holy.

—Robert J. Barbera, President, Barbera Foundation
—Ken LaZebnik, Founding Editor, The Mentoris Project

Chapter One

A STRANGE SIGHT IN CHICAGO

"Are you seeing what I'm seeing?"

The police officer speaking was slightly older than the other, and at this moment, also slightly drunk.

"If you're seeing three nuns with a long twine marking off a piece of property, then yes," said the younger man. "But what the devil are they up to?"

It was 1904 and Chicago had just declared a crackdown on the rampant problem of police officers drinking on the job and doing nothing to stop crime. The younger officer took this quite seriously and had sworn off the drink two days before—today his inebriated partner irritated him badly.

It was early dawn—the red sun peeked out between gray wisps of clouds into a cool morning mist over Lake Michigan. The two officers slowly approached the nuns, the older policeman listing slightly to the left. To him, the nun in charge seemed to be incredibly short, yet even in the dim light he could sense her bustling energy.

"Good morning, Sister!" said the older officer loudly. "Can you tell me what you could possibly be doing at this hour, in this place? You're looking slightly suspicious, if I do say so!"

Mother Cabrini stopped and turned to the officers, noting the older one swaying slightly. "*Buongiorno c'è qualcosa che non va?* We're finding out just how dishonest the men are who are selling this property to us," she said with a smile, noting their interest. Although she could speak English, she still had a strong Italian accent. "We are Missionary Sisters of the Sacred Heart, and we're about to purchase this land and that building to establish a hospital."

"Why, that's very good and kind of you!" said the younger police officer. "But what is that twine for?"

"We are making our purchase on a specific size of land, and I've asked my Sisters to help me measure the dimensions again. I'm sorry to tell you that the seller has tried to trick us by moving the surveyor marks so that we get less land than we've been bargaining for."

"I see. Do you need our help with anything, Sister?" said the older policeman, suddenly indignant at the thought of anyone swindling a nun.

"No, thank you, Officer. I think we've confirmed what I suspected—he's trying to cheat us. We will meet with the owner this morning, and I will not hesitate to tell him exactly what I think of his treatment of the Missionary Sisters of the Sacred Heart."

"He should be ashamed of himself," said the younger officer, shaking his head. After assurances that she and the Sisters could find their way back to their lodgings easily, the two officers walked away.

Mother Cabrini watched them go—she had smelled the alcohol on the older one's breath, and said a quick prayer for their safety.

She was not bitter that the seller had attempted to deceive her, but she was glad she'd followed her instincts to measure the property. It would not be the first time—nor the last—that a man would try to swindle her in business dealings. When she exposed their tricks and confronted the men directly, she watched them shrink under her blue-eyed gaze in shame.

Mother Frances Xavier Cabrini was far from the small village in Northern Italy where she was born and raised. She was in America, where, now at age fifty-four, she demonstrated her skills as a shrewd and successful businesswoman.

They had been honed for decades—she had already negotiated with many businessmen and officials around the world for buildings and property to be used by her Missionary Sisters of the Sacred Heart. Intelligent, charming, generous, adventurous, *La Madre* was petite but fierce. She would not back down in her negotiations when the well-being—both physical and spiritual—of Italian immigrants and their families was at stake.

Her eyes sparkled as she watched the police officers walk off into Chicago's city landscape. She knew that in a matter of years this hospital would be ready and would be named Columbus Hospital, after the first Italian immigrant to America. But she had no way of knowing that this would be one of many hospitals she would build in her lifetime—and the one in which she would die years later.

And she did not know that she would become America's first saint. In fact, in honor of her astounding accomplishments, she would be called the Patron Saint of Immigrants. Now as the sun rose on the empty lot, Mother Cabrini calculated that in several hours she would find the office of the crooked property sellers who had tried to cheat her, and confront them.

She relished the thought.

Chapter Two

A WEAK GIRL WITH A STRONG SPIRIT

Years before, little Francesca Cabrini—called *Ceccina* by her family—sat on a grassy patch of ground near the river and arranged purple violets in a small paper boat she had made. Glancing around to make sure she was alone, the six-year-old girl began to speak to the flowers about the missions she had prepared for them. "*Carissime Sorelle.* My dear little one, you must go to England," she said to the first flower. Picking up another she said, "You must be brave and sail all the way to Brazil to help the poor children. And you," she whispered to a small flower, "must go all the way to China!"

Francesca Maria had been born prematurely in 1850, one of eleven children to Agostino and Stella Cabrini, in the village of Sant'Angelo Lodigiano in Northern Italy. Her sister Rosa read her stories about brave missionaries, how they traveled to far away places to teach savages about Jesus. Sitting on the bank of the Venera River, near the home of her uncle, Reverend Luigi Oldini, she turned her wide blue eyes upward. She felt at peace in this isolated spot—the quiet soothed her as she stared into the blue horizon across the fields where farmers worked. *When can I become a missionary, and sail to other countries?*

She was a small child, with a round face, wide blue eyes, and blond hair. Her temperament was calm. She was obedient—wanting to do what her parents asked simply because she loved them very much. She was an observant child, and saw that her mother and father worked hard, as did most of the grown-ups in her small village.

In the evenings her father read the Bible out loud to the family, and later, in bed as she was falling asleep, Francesca would go over these stories in her mind, picturing herself as a character in them. She would find a baby lamb and cradle it in her arms as she walked beside Jesus. She would run to help the poor beggar left on the side of the road, and help the Good Samaritan to the inn. She gasped as Jesus came out of the cloud wearing glowing white robes. He waved to Francesca and then reached down to give her a tiny cross.

Francesca was sick often, mostly with breathing difficulties, and often she just felt weak and tired. But she could be as strong-willed as her older sister Rosa, who acted like she was her mother. Rosa was a harsh disciplinarian to Francesca and their little brother, and she was as adamant as their parents that reading and practicing arithmetic came before playing outside.

Ceccina liked it when Rosa told her stories about missionaries, but she didn't like it that Rosa always wanted to know what she was doing, where she was going. Francesca preferred to climb trees, or roam about the village and the nearby fields as she wished. Like now, for instance—it was so much fun that her older sister had no idea that she was down here by the water.

Ceccina carefully slid down the bank of the rushing river with her paper boats and stepped onto a large flat rock on the edge of the water. She looked down into the water—it was dark. She knelt to place the first little boat in the little stream, leaning far out and stretching her arm over the water. She tipped her body just a bit more forward…

She could feel the weight of her small body shift too far—she flung her arms down to try to catch the edge of the rock, but it was too late. Falling forward into the cold rushing water, Francesca screamed as loudly as she could. The force of the fast-moving water swept her downstream and she tried to grab something—anything—but could not.

"*Aiuto!*" she cried out, then she tumbled under the water and when she gasped, water filled her mouth and throat. She turned herself face up again and coughed, spurting out the water, then cried again, "*Aiuto! Help!*"

A man's voice replied somewhere above to the left on the river bank, and then people were shouting. She opened her mouth again to shout back but the water filled it, and as Francesca gasped she saw black blotches and then lost consciousness.

When she opened her eyes, the girl was surrounded by the familiar faces of neighboring farmers and their wives who lifted her up, grasping her hands and shoulders. She was cold and someone wrapped her in a blanket. "Jesus saved me…" mumbled Francesca. "I know he saved me, he wanted me to live." The villagers looked at each other.

"Do you remember the time of the earthquake, when we found her praying?" said one woman quietly to another. The other nodded, staring at the girl. Just a few years earlier, when their village was jolted by an afternoon earthquake, adults desperately searched for every child. One was missing—Ceccina. Finally, they came upon her calmly praying in a corner of her house. The girl was strangely unafraid, completely absorbed in her quiet prayers. She had survived unhurt—again. The women whispered that the girl seemed to be protected somehow.

∾

When Agostino and Stella Cabrini heard that their Ceccina had nearly drowned, they were terrified and thanked God for her safety and survival. Many children died young in this village—the couple had lost nine of theirs. A pious and strong-hearted man, Agostino had suffered deeply the losses of these children. He never stopped working in his fields, never stopped greeting his neighbors whenever he passed them, never stopped caring for his wife, but everyone saw the cloud of sadness in his eyes and the downward slope of his shoulders.

He and Stella doted on their surviving children—Maddalena, a girl born with severe brain damage, who needed constant care, and their beloved boy Giovanni Battista. They fretted over Francesca's weakness and ill health, often keeping her inside. Rosa, their oldest, was solemn and dutiful, more so because she had witnessed the deaths of her other siblings.

She had learned embroidery and taught Ceccina how to do so too—the two working on intricate patterns in lace and designs on linen. When their father was busy, Rosa read the Bible and other books aloud to her siblings in the evenings, and secretly dreamed of becoming a nun.

Rosa's life was not easy. Her mother relied heavily on her to do most of the cleaning and cooking. The women of her village consoled Stella with the loss of each child, but Stella slowly withdrew into a quiet sadness. Her only joy now was to teach her children at home—reading, simple arithmetic, and the little history and geography that she knew. It was increasingly difficult for Stella to keep up with even the simple chores, and Rosa took on more and more as she minded Ceccina and Giovanni Battista and cared for Maddalena.

One evening, Rosa approached her mother, who was resting on her small bed. "Mama," she said. "I want to tell you that I have only one dream for my future."

Stella turned to look lovingly at her daughter's face. "Tell me, my dear Rosa, what is it you dream?"

"My dream, Mama, is to become a nun."

Stella loved her oldest daughter with her whole heart, but could not allow her to leave her side, especially with Maddalena's many needs. There was too much to be done for one woman in this house. "My daughter, you cannot leave us. Make this home your convent."

Stella closed her eyes and turned away. Tears welled up and her heart hurt. She knew her mother struggled, but she felt her spirit breaking. Finally, she wiped away her tears and resolved, *I will do the work of Jesus here, in this house, in this town.*

But over time, disappointment hardened Rosa. She became strict with her siblings, watching them constantly and ordering them to do their chores and schoolwork. She almost never let Francesca out of her sight because she seemed a bit too independent.

July 1, 1857, was a warm summer day in the village of Sant'Angelo. Sunlight splashed off the tiled rooftops and the cobblestone streets. In her room, Rosa combed and oiled Francesca's blond hair to make it look dark, and then helped her get dressed. Ceccina was quiet—she was to receive the Sacrament of Confirmation today, an honor. Her family washed and dressed in their finest clothing, and together they walked to the village church.

Francesca was seven, and small for her age. As she knelt down at the rail near the altar with the other children, she was the smallest of them all. She looked up, as she often did toward the sky when she was outside playing. Soft light filtered through the stained-glass windows high above. She was at peace—as big and complicated as the world was, she felt utterly safe. She listened to the familiar voice of the bishop and became aware of a loving presence all around her. The bishop leaned down to anoint her forehead, and suddenly Francesca felt as if a warm cloak were being placed around her shoulders. She lost the sensation of being on the ground. *I know it is you, Holy Ghost, who is here to protect me,* she thought. She stood up with the other children, but she was disoriented. Was it day or night? Was she inside or outside? Who was with her besides the bishop and the children now filing out of the church?

Something had just happened, but what was it?

Agostino and Stella were farmers, earning money by selling their produce in the town market. They worked constantly. They were generous to their neighbors, sharing produce with those who had nothing, but they were frugal in their business and had done well. Beyond their own village, however, Italy was in turmoil.

Austria had invaded the Lombardy region in 1869 and now ruled the northwest areas of Lombardy and Venetia. Even residents of Sant'Angelo were well aware of this, because Austrian soldiers stopped in the village—several of them inviting themselves to stay in the Cabrini household. Though the family really had no choice in the matter, Agostino politely made sure the soldiers were comfortable and had plenty to eat. Months later, to the amusement of the villagers, the same soldiers passed hastily through the village again—this time in retreat—too much in a hurry to stay even an hour in the town.

"Say nothing," Agostino counseled his wife and children. He wanted them to remain quiet on the subject of politics, especially because people who called themselves nationalists were against the Church and all its power. It was well known that Agostino was Catholic. He made sure to sidestep public arguments. But he and Stella were always aware of the potential danger in being known as Catholic. They wanted Rosa, Ceccina, and Giovanni Battista to be educated so that they could live well in the world. When Francesca was thirteen, they decided it was time to send their youngest daughter to a convent school: Daughters of the Sacred Heart, located in the nearby town of Arluno. The nuns there had a reputation of being kind and patient with their students, while encouraging the young women to think and express themselves intelligently. Agostino and Stella hoped it would help their inquisitive little Ceccina to focus her mind on studies. Stella and Rosa had given her lessons at home for years. Now she had learned all she could from her mother and sister and was eager for more.

"*I have been to China!* I have seen the people who live in the mountains and have traveled that land to share the words of Jesus Christ, our savior!"

Francesca spun around to find the person who shouted these words. It felt as if he were speaking to her and to her alone. She located him right away—the man was wearing a black cassock and his long dark hair blew about in the wind. His eyes were bright and dark, and he spoke with a half smile as he surveyed the village crowd. The visitor to Sant'Angelo was standing on a wooden box in the town square, addressing the crowd of townspeople who stopped to listen.

It was just a few weeks before Francesca was to depart for Arluno and to her new convent school. As usual, the girl had accompanied her parents to the village market early in the morning, where she would help them sell the produce from their small farm. Now she stared at the man, who stood tall and straight, calling people to come hear his story. Drawn by his deep voice, Francesca stepped toward him to better hear. He was loud—as if he knew that hardly any of them would care about his story or even believe him, yet he was compelled to tell it. He was used to traveling alone and now insisted this audience hear what he had witnessed and experienced.

"I have seen many foreign lands, traveled by sea," he said, his voice booming. "I am a missionary, and I was guided by Jesus himself to share his words with all who did not yet know his grace and love."

Captivated, Francesca moved closer and listened while he told of being hungry and exhausted while he walked from town to town, over mountains and across wide rivers to remote villages, hidden from civilization. He met with men, women, and even children who had no religion.

No religion? Francesca was riveted. *How could people have no religion?* With the help of translators, the man said, he brought the message of the Catholic religion to peasants of foreign lands and showed them how they could be saved from their sins. "*Ceccina!*" called Stella. "Come and help us—you don't need to listen to that man." Francesca turned back to her family reluctantly. The man's words were electrifying. He was a missionary, and had been to China!

≈

Francesca was nervous about leaving home and the world she knew. But after a few weeks in the convent school, she adored the nuns at the Daughters of Sacred Heart. She loved the lessons—geography and history were her favorite subjects—which fed her quick, intelligent mind. Hours disappeared when she studied the pages of geography books, memorizing the names of the highest mountain peaks in the world, and tracing her fingers over the boundaries of Argentina, Chile, Spain, England, and France. In her daydreams she could almost see these places, especially the mountain peaks, such as of Miranda and Tenerife in Spain.

One day I might climb these mountains, she thought.

At school, she found an atlas and books filled with real-life stories about explorers who had traveled to far-off countries beyond the familiar small villages of the Lombardy region. She read about native tribes in South America who still lived as their ancestors had hundreds of years ago.

She discovered a book about China and tried to memorize the names of provinces and cities of this vast country. She wondered: *Exactly where did the missionaries go? What were their routes, and how did they survive?* Her teachers drew the girls into discussions and encouraged them to learn about cultures and customs foreign to their own. Francesca was an eager student, taking in all she learned and basking in the kindness that the nuns offered. In her imagination, she was already a missionary, traveling far and wide around the world.

With each year, young Francesca's confidence grew. While she was in school, her sister Rosa had become a teacher. Now seeing a chance to earn money for her parents, to keep learning, and help other girls do the same, Francesca decided she would train to be a teacher too.

But after five years at the school, she really only wanted one thing: to join the nuns and be as much like them as possible. She made a formal request to join the order, but her request was turned down. Stung and hurt, she returned home. Was it her physical weakness? She was sick often, and could not run around with the other girls too long before she needed to stop and sit down. Heartbroken, Francesca cried to herself: *I know with my whole soul that I am called to be a spouse of Jesus. Why am I being denied?*

Chapter Three

A GIFT FOR TEACHING

"*I'm going to be a teacher.*" Francesca practiced saying the words out loud. The reality was sinking in. Ever since she received the news of her rejection from the Daughters of the Sacred Heart, Francesca had suffered in silent disappointment. But now her schooling was completed—she had packed her bag, said her goodbyes to her friends and beloved teachers. At last, she stepped down and away from the school and began her long walk back on a hard, dusty road to Sant'Angelo.

Fields of golden wheat undulated in the breeze to her right, and cows lazily grazed in the hazy afternoon sunlight to her left. But Francesca hardly noticed. She looked down at her already dusty shoes walking, one step in front of the other, toward home. In her mind she was going over the question again and again: *Why was her request to join this order denied?*

Suffering, she knew, was part of being a missionary and of following Jesus. And she very much aspired to perform "mortifications," ways in which Catholics purposely suffered—by fasting, sleeping on hard wood, living in extreme poverty, even lashing their own bodies. Her suffering right now was severe disappointment at not being able to become a nun. But to question the rejection, was that going against God's will?

In the quiet of her solitary walking, Francesca shifted her thoughts to the fact that she had passed her examinations and was now officially qualified to be a teacher. She had had many teachers—her mother, Rosa, the Sisters. Teachers were sacred. They could change a girl's life forever by just offering praise at little things well done, and by opening up the world through books and stories about other countries. That's what had happened to her. These kind and knowledgeable nuns had fueled Francesca's passion to be a missionary, although it still seemed like a far-off dream to her. Of the girls she knew in Sant'Angelo, some were already married and had a baby or two, and some never got to go to school at all because they had to work every day on their family's farms. She already knew in her bones that this was not the life she wanted. Francesca had also known girls not much older than Rosa who had died in childbirth.

To be a teacher—this is a privilege! Francesca thought. And she already knew that it was one way she could explore the world. She relaxed a little and allowed herself to feel pride in the years of her education with the nuns. It had been difficult at times, but her teachers had been so encouraging and delighted in her appetite to learn. They had given her and the other girls a rare freedom: to be as inquisitive and intelligent as they wished, with no boy or man to judge or stop them. From this moment on, Francesca vowed that she would add the words "Elementary School Teacher" beneath her signature in any letter she wrote. It was autumn, 1868. This would be a proud day for her family too.

She arrived at the door of her parents' home by late afternoon and eagerly pushed it open. Her whole family was there, preparing to eat an early dinner, and looked up in surprise when she entered the house. Stella rushed to greet her daughter, with Agostino close behind. Rosa nodded at her with a smile, but was quiet. Giovanni Battista laughed and jumped up to give her a hug. Even Maddalena seemed to pay attention and stared at Francesca and at the family commotion.

Francesca waved her examination papers in the air and shared the good news. But when she looked into Rosa's eyes, she knew instantly something was wrong. When she had a moment, she pulled her sister aside.

"You can't hide it, something is wrong—tell me!" she demanded.

"Can't you see it?" Rosa said quietly. "Mama and Papa—neither one is in good health. I'm worried." Now Francesca was quiet.

"I did see," she said, thinking now how tired they'd both seemed. "But what is wrong?" Rosa shook her head; she didn't know.

Happy to be home, Francesca returned easily to her life with her family, helping with the chores, caring for Maddalena, and maintaining the spiritual practices she had become accustomed to with the Sisters. Sundays were always especially happy, because the family attended church together.

"*Help! Rosa, Ceccina!*" Stella wailed early one Sunday morning. The daughters ran into their parents' bedroom to find their father slumped to one side in the bed. He could not right himself—half his body had gone slack. The village doctor was called and he confirmed that Agostino had suffered a massive stroke.

Rosa and Francesca exchanged glances, knowing that their life was changed forever. In the following days, weeks, and months, they cared for their debilitated father as he struggled to do even minor tasks in the house. Stella, heartbroken and overwhelmed, became withdrawn and the sisters ministered to both—attending their physical needs, and praying with them.

In a year, Agostino died, and months later, Stella died too, at age sixty-two. Their children were bereft. Giovanni Battista kept up the farm work, but he had no real interest in it now that his father was gone. Watching his older sisters, he had decided that he too wanted to be a teacher. Stunned by the loss of both parents, Francesca's grief was heavy. She tried to visualize her future, but could not do so.

In the spring of 1871, a highly contagious chicken pox outbreak swept through Sant'Angelo. Francesca, eighteen, realizing how many of her neighbors and friends were sick, decided to do whatever she could to help the people who were ill and her missionary spirit stirred. She brought warm bread and broth to her sick neighbors, cleaned their blisters, and placed cool cloths on their foreheads while urging them to eat. But in the evening at home, Rosa became stern. "Why do you put yourself in such danger? You think you are doing good, but you too will soon be sick and then you will be no help at all." Francesca lowered her eyes and thought: *Jesus compels me to go out to the sick. So it is Jesus who will protect me.*

Both sisters were right. Within weeks, Francesca was ill with chicken pox, and could not get out of bed. Watching Francesca feverishly toss and turn, Rosa was tempted to remind her how foolish she had been. "*Gesù Cristo, posso sentire voi vicin a me,*" whispered Francesca in her feverish sleep. "I can feel you near me. Where you call me I will go…" Rosa stared at her delirious sister curiously. How could she admonish her?

Not long after she recovered, Francesca was visited by the local priest, who asked if she would be a substitute teacher in the village of Vidardo a mile away. She readily said yes—she and her siblings needed money and this was her first chance to use her teaching skills. She met with Vidardo's parish rector, Don Antonio Serrati. As he explained her duties, young Francesca's thoughts drifted. Of course she would take this job, but in her heart she could feel the desire to do something far bigger than to be a substitute teacher. She wanted to climb mountain peaks, cross rushing rivers, and bring the love of Jesus to people who had never had religion! Little did she know that the man sitting before her would be a guide toward that very journey, and in fact, that her journey had already begun.

Within a few days, her teaching post started in the small wood-frame schoolhouse. Though awkward and overly strict with her young students at first, Francesca eventually relaxed and won them over with kindness and her infectious enthusiasm for learning. Teaching religion held some risk, Francesca knew quite well, as the anti-cleric government officials frowned upon it. She made sure to use her quietest voice for these lessons.

Serrati observed Francesca's natural style of teaching the young people in his parish, and was impressed by how engaged her students were becoming in their studies. When he learned that she had requested again to join the Daughters of the Sacred Heart, he immediately calculated the loss this would mean for his community. He exerted his influence to make sure the nuns rejected her request, citing her physical weakness.

Not long after that, Francesca offered herself to the Canossian Sisters at Crema, but once again Serrati secretly blocked her acceptance. Twice denied, Francesca was devastated and in her nightly prayers she appealed to Jesus to reveal his true purpose for her.

Soon another opportunity arose: Serrati wanted to tap Francesca's obvious ability to inspire and lead and he went to visit her at the end of one school day to tell her about it. "Francesca, I am soon going to be transferred to the town of Codogno—the orphanage and convent there, called House of Providence, is apparently not being well run. It needs help. I want to ask you to go there, to be part of the community and to do what you can to assist in the administration and regain order."

Francesca listened intently as Monsignor Serrati described the problems at the orphanage. "The two administrators have mismanaged it terribly, and furthermore they're too harsh with the orphans and young religious women. I'm afraid these administrators, well, they are personally difficult."

Francesca looked down, hoping to hide her feelings. She knew she should say yes to this proposition, but what about her dreams of being a missionary? Was that going to be an unfulfilled dream forever? Still reeling from her second obstacle toward becoming a nun, Francesca felt the calling to Jesus more than ever before. Yet she understood that Monsignor Serrati was giving her a chance to save the young orphans and convent girls from a terrible fate. She knew the rule of obedience for nuns, and she adapted it to her own life. "Of course, Monsignor," she said. "I will to go to Codogno. When would you like me to begin?"

Chapter Four

CONFLICT IN THE HOUSE OF PROVIDENCE

"Could this be the young Francesca Cabrini who is coming to help us?" said Teresa Calza, a tall, thin woman, peering out the window to the street below while raising a skeptical eyebrow. A young woman was trudging up the tree-lined cobblestone street toward the orphanage. It was a hot mid-August afternoon in 1874, and she stopped to rest a moment in the shade of a tree. She turned her face toward the large red brick structure ahead, which housed orphans and young novices—her new home.

Antonia Tondini and Teresa Calza were administrators of the House of Providence. As the director, Antonia particularly enjoyed sitting in her large office behind an imposing wood desk. She did not answer her colleague at first, then turned to look out the window. "What a weak-looking woman. What could she do for us?"

"Extreme discipline, outbursts of anger, mismanagement of money..." In her mind, Francesca reviewed the litany of problems she'd learned about her new place of work as she made her way up

the street. Apparently, Antonia Tondini had donated a large sum of money to found the House of Providence, so the local clergy could not force her to change—they even insisted she and Teresa become nuns but that had had no effect.

Francesca was determined to do as she was told: to bring peace and order to this place. She would do it, with God's help. As she resolutely headed toward the convent and orphanage, she whispered to herself: *"Help me, Jesus, bring love and joy to this place."*

It was now late summer and very hot. About twenty orphans and five young women who were religious aspirants lived in the House of Providence, but Antonia or Teresa took no joy in the life there and viewed their work as a burden. Neither of them liked children and they did not even pretend to. They preferred the orphans to be compliant and cause no trouble—and punished them severely when they disobeyed. Bereft of any real religious sensibility, they made jokes about people who were true believers.

"Come in!" said Teresa Calza, opening the front door when Francesca finally arrived. Startled at first by Francesca's big blue eyes, Teresa quickly regained her composure and invited the young woman into the house. Antonia, who was short and out of breath, chimed in with a shrill welcome behind her. Francesca smiled nervously. Hearing the thumps of little running feet, she glanced up just in time to see two little girls disappear from the top of a stairway, then pop their heads around the corner again to peek at her.

"Go to your room!" hissed Antonia at the children.

Turning back to Francesca with a strained smile, Antonia beckoned to her to come down the hall to her new room. Once alone to unpack her bag, Francesca wondered about what she had already seen. That sharpness in speaking to the children was unpleasant. She saw how frightened they were, and how they cringed at Antonia's voice. Francesca reminded herself, *I'm here to do the work of Jesus, to be kind and loving to these children and young women, to teach them the way I was taught.*

The next morning she met Antonia in her office for instructions. The administrator was stern, her face was joyless: Francesca was to report directly to her to plan the educational programs. She was to teach several classes of children, and to offer professional guidance to the other teachers and spiritual lessons to the young women. Meeting concluded.

Teresa Calza then brought Francesca to a small classroom where the children were already seated. Stepping to the front of the room, Francesca glanced around for books, paper, or pencils—but saw none. "Good morning," she said to the upturned faces looking at her apprehensively. "If you please, will each of you tell me your name?" she said.

Silence.

Wide eyes stared at her, and Francesca saw that they were frightened. She was quiet for a moment, thinking of times when she had been a nervous student and a teacher had kindly drawn her out. "My name is Francesca Maria Cabrini and I come from Sant'Angelo."

Still, the children looked at her silently. Francesca realized that if she were ever to be trusted, she would have to help them to relax. "On my way here, I saw a donkey in the field, and two goats," she said, on a whim. "And then I saw a horse eating grass under a tree. Can you name other animals you've seen in the countryside?"

One girl shyly raised her hand and said, "I saw a chicken yesterday."

"I saw an orange cat on the fence this morning!" said another child.

"I like cows," said a small boy in the back of the room.

"I do too," said Francesca, looking into his eyes. "For today, let's see if we can name twenty animals, and how many legs and ears they have. Tomorrow, we'll learn how to spell some animal names."

The next day the children began to offer answers to Francesca's simple questions as she guided them through fundamental lessons. She found paper and pencils in a hallway closet and brought them to the class so that her students could draw and write alphabet letters. In a matter of weeks, the students were spelling words for common objects in their surroundings. Francesca invited them to play guessing games with homemade cards, matching words with pictures of animals, foods, and other objects.

She was called to Antonia's office one afternoon. "You are not to encourage these children to play games in class," the director burst out angrily as soon as she saw Francesca. "This is not for amusement. These orphans need to speak only when they are asked a question. They're not to leave their chairs, they're not to draw…stop encouraging them immediately. In fact, I will take over this class for the rest of the week to restore order."

Francesca began to protest, but Antonia raised her hand. "No! There is no discussion. Please go to your room." As she closed the office door behind her, Francesca turned the corner and nearly collided with two young women—Cecelia and

Maria—who had obviously been eavesdropping. They had come to live at the House of Providence the year before, hoping to become nuns.

"We heard everything!" exclaimed Maria in a whisper. "You are so good with the children, and it's the first time they've been allowed to be happy. You've gotten some of them to speak even though they have never opened their mouths before! Please, may we talk with you?" Francesca hurried down the hall, motioning for them to follow her to a secluded spot in the garden.

Maria spoke in hushed tones about the harsh rules of the director and her assistant, how the teachers were intimidated, and children were sometimes denied food as punishment. They'd been given almost no religious training, and Antonia was prone to angry tirades that frightened everyone. She and Cecilia pleaded to Francesca for help.

Hearing all this deeply distressed Francesca, but confirmed what she had already observed. To openly defy Antonia, though, would certainly make matters worse. Yet she would certainly never abandon her duty to the children nor to these young women who craved spiritual guidance, so she agreed to meet secretly with them. And soon they found time to pray as a small group and read Scripture when they knew the administrators were asleep. The happier they became, the more excited Francesca became as a teacher. She not only found new books for them to read, but also taught them embroidery and sewing as a way to calm themselves.

Monsignor Serrati sent frequent letters, urging Francesca to inspire the Sisters of Providence in Codogno to keep up with all religious practices and education programs. Francesca took these directions seriously and convinced Antonia to allow her to lead Sunday vesper services. She organized retreats for women in the surrounding villages and taught the Spiritual Exercises of Saint Ignatius. She encouraged the young women—some still only teenagers—to devote their lives to God with constant prayer and by helping the younger ones. Together they developed Sunday school classes for children as well as adults.

While always outwardly respectful to Antonia and Teresa, Francesca forged ahead in doing what Serrati asked. The children adored her, and the young religious women admired her too, becoming more confident and happy in her presence. At twenty-four, Francesca was determined to set things right at the House of Providence and she finally realized her wish to be a nun. She received the religious habit, and new name: Sister Saveria Angelica.

She was now officially a Sister of Providence! She decided to sleep on boards, an ascetic practice to align herself with Jesus's own sacrifice. But after a few months, she gave this up when she found that it just made her so tired she could not function. Instead, she told the young women that she realized it was "diligence in small things that led to the road of holiness."

Antonia and Teresa were displeased about these developments and grew more suspicious than ever of Francesca's motives. Their resentment sharpened when Bishop Domenico Gelmini of Lodi appointed Sister Saveria Angelica as the Superior of the House of Providence—impossibly, the two women were expected to answer directly to Francesca.

Outraged at their displacement, Antonia and Teresa plotted to obstruct Francesca's every effort. They were openly hostile, and told lies about her to anyone who would listen. The young nuns became so afraid for the safety of their new Superior that they took turns guarding her room at night. In any case, sleep was difficult. Attempting to bear up under the constant unpleasantness, Francesca sought comfort in writing about her situation to her sister Rosa, and in praying.

One evening, feeling especially restless, she went to the chapel to pray. The children had been put to bed, and the House was quiet and dark. Francesca approached the simple altar and knelt on the stone floor. Closing her eyes and clasping her hands beneath her chin, she entered an interior darkness and asked Jesus for strength, and for forgiveness in failing to do more in his name. A quietness took over and she was no longer saying or thinking words. A familiar warm comfort surrounded her in the depth of this meditation, and with every breath she could sense the presence of God.

Suddenly, the tapping of steps approaching penetrated her meditation, and then…"*What are you praying about?*" Antonia shouted, just inches away from Francesca's face. "What are you saying? I demand that you tell me this instant what you are praying about!" Francesca opened her eyes, rose slowly, and turned toward the woman. She felt the power of God in her heart as she looked upon Antonia's face, distorted with emotion. The young nun had never been defiant, had never retaliated in word or deed to Antonia, and she would not do so now. But Antonia had just shown that even the sanctity of prayer meant nothing to her.

Francesca walked around Antonia, who glared at her, and returned to her room, locking the door behind her. After that night, Antonia's attacks on Francesca were more open—she called her names, threatened her, and mocked her in front of the children. Francesca tensed whenever she saw Antonia or Teresa, and avoided them whenever she could. She bore their hatred, month after month—after all, she told herself, missionaries endured much worse suffering, as of course, did Jesus. But the strain made her unable to eat, and her sleep was fitful. Already pale, she now began to appear ill to the young nuns who counted on her so much.

"Good morning, students," Francesca greeted the children one morning in early April of 1880. "Today we'll begin with geography." As the children pulled out their handmade maps, Francesca heard Antonia's voice shriek somewhere down the hall. The familiar ranting voice rose, and all of them could hear the woman berate a child for not dressing properly. Suddenly, Francesca felt herself stumble sideways, and sensed water rushing all around her. Just as when she had fallen into the river as a girl, she felt herself drowning. The cold water was covering her face, slipping into her mouth and nose…she could not breathe…The children shouted and then ran for help when they saw Francesca collapse to the floor. Three other teachers rushed into the classroom and lifted her up and carried to her bed. A doctor was called, who after examining her insisted that she remain in bed for two weeks.

"How are you feeling?" asked Cecelia, who had come to check on Francesca.

"Strong today," replied Francesca. "I miss everyone and the children—what is happening? Tell me."

Cecelia hesitated and then blurted out that Antonia had stopped paying the hired staff, and yet had been seen taking money from the House of Providence safe and handing it to her nephew, who had come to visit. Francesca sighed, and struggled to pull herself up in bed. "Do you know this to be true?" she asked.

"I do, yes," said the nun.

Francesca got out of bed to write a letter to Bishop Gelmini. It was time for him to intervene. When he received the news, the Bishop at last understood the terrible situation at the House of Providence. He shook his head—how had it come to this? He was amazed that Francesca had persisted there for six long years, and now he had get her out of there.

Father Giuliani, who supposedly guided the spiritual life of the House of Providence, realized now how far it had fallen. "I beg you from my heart to forgive my many failings," he wrote to Francesca, "and to pray to the Lord to pardon me."

Francesca's heart swelled—of course she forgave him. But the words in that letter from Bishop Gelmini caused tears to fill her eyes. Now might be the time, he suggested, for her to create a religious community of her own. It would be among the first orders of women missionaries in the world.

Chapter Five

A NEW ORDER OF WOMEN MISSIONARIES

She did not mind sweeping the dusty floors or scrubbing the dirty windows. She did not mind being continually hungry because there was little food to eat. Quite the opposite: Francesca was jubilant. She was thirty years old, and had received official permission to start her own order with seven young nuns who had followed her from the troubled House of Providence.

To signify this new beginning, she decided to change her name: She was now Mother Francesca Saveria Cabrini. Saveria was the Italian feminine version of Xavier; Cabrini deeply revered Saint Francis Xavier, a missionary like herself who had longed to go to China. He had traveled to India and Japan and helped found the Society of Jesus, later known as the Jesuits.

Young, devout, energetic, the eight women exulted in their new reality: They would be missionaries at last. Monsignor Serrati had generously given Francesca money to purchase a building in Codogno. And she found the perfect location—an abandoned Franciscan friary on Via Unione in the town of Codogno. It was a two-story building with an interior courtyard and covered walkway that had been uninhabited for years. Now the women swept and scrubbed energetically. It was theirs!

Sister Salesia and Sister Agostina cleaned a room for the chapel on the ground floor, and set up a simple wood table with two candles in the middle. Mother Cabrini and Sister Pesserini determined which rooms would be for the orphans they planned to take in, and Sister Colomba, Sister Veronica, and Sister Francescina cleaned out two small rooms for their own sleeping quarters. Sister Gaetania scrubbed the kitchen and, with money donated by Bishop Gelmini, planned to purchase food at the market. They had no lamps or furniture yet in their new convent, and had to share one fork and one spoon when eating. But this poverty was all just as it should be—they were missionaries, and enthusiastically accepted the meager existence of this life.

In just a few days Monsignor Serrati was to arrive for his first visit to the convent, and the sisters wanted it to sparkle. Neighbors joined to help plant flowers in the patches of ground at the entrance, and soon the convent began to look lived in and cared for.

Sunday, November 14, 1880, finally arrived and early that morning Monsignor Serrati stood at their doorstep. He was greeted by Mother Cabrini and the Sisters, who all wore dark habits with large black bows tied under their chins. He was delighted to be shown around the new quarters by the young nuns, and presented them with a Decree of Foundation from Bishop Gelmini. He then said Mass in the small chapel.

Francesca's eyes filled with tears as he blessed this new foundation, and her heart beat with excitement. After all the years of difficulty at the House of Providence, working around the obstacles constantly thrown in her path, she could now give all her energy to the work she was meant to do, in Jesus's name.

After the service, Serrati asked Mother Cabrini to stroll with him around the cobbled streets of Codogno. It was a chilly, clear autumn day. They passed the small connected homes and open piazzas. As they walked, Mother Cabrini told her mentor that she had decided on the name of her order: the Institute of the Salesian Missionaries of the Sacred Heart.

"Tell me, my dear, I am curious about this name," Serrati said with some hesitation in his voice. "What is your reasoning in your choice?"

"Of course, to honor the faith and kindness of Saint Francis de Sales," she replied, referring to the Bishop of Geneva who had faced many obstacles in his efforts to bring people to the Church. She was well aware that Serrati revered the saint.

"But, I am questioning the word *missionary*..." he said with worry crinkling his face.

"Why, that is what we are, that is our purpose—it has been my purpose since I can remember," said Francesca.

She stopped walking and turned toward her friend. "Of course, yes, I understand," said Serrati, looking directly into the sparkling blue eyes he knew so well. She was the most determined woman he had ever known—she was intelligent and driven, now apparently more so than ever. He had seen her endure years of struggle, yet she always seemed to keep her bright outlook on life.

"But the name missionary is identified with men," he said timidly, "and some clerics say it is not fitting for your new order."

"We are missionaries, I cannot pretend that we are anything else," she said. She was angry, but remembered how her father Agostino had taught her that sometimes silence was a more wise response than an outburst.

It would not be wise to say anything more. Monsignor had been her ally for years, and she was grateful every day for his kindness, friendship, and support. Missionary work was *God's calling for her* and she was not going to allow anyone to keep her from it—in name or deed—ever again.

Women could be missionaries, about this she was certain.

Mother Cabrini, or *La Madre*, as the Sisters often called her, organized a daily life of practice for the nuns, emphasizing charity—for each other, for children, for town residents, for everyone. She asked the sisters to meet for prayer and meditation every day, and maintain silence as much as possible. Devoted to the pope, and relying on Monsignor Serrati and Bishop Gelmini for their wisdom and advice, Mother Cabrini thought constantly about the best way to train her Sisters—or her "Daughters," as she affectionately referred to them—to become courageous missionaries.

The pain of being attacked with hurtful gossip and resentment in the House of Providence was still fresh in her memory. Cabrini entreated her missionary sisters to envision themselves as a vibrant community, unified in their work and purpose. Because they had limited money—and most likely always would—she taught them how to manage the convent frugally and simply.

The nuns thrived under Mother Cabrini's kind direction, and were as dedicated as she was in educating children and caring for neighbors in need. The reputation of this energetic convent soon spread, and young women came to join from the surrounding villages, attracted by the missionary spirit.

≈

Two years passed and the convent grew, filling to capacity with orphans and new postulants—young women from every social class who sought out this unique way of life. One morning, Mother Cabrini was hurrying down the covered walkway to meet with several young women from Codogno who had come to join the order, when suddenly she stopped. Sunlight filled the courtyard, and from every direction she could hear the bubbling voices of a happy, busy community. The laughter of children playing outside, next to a fountain. The clanging of pots in the kitchen as Sister Gaetania prepared food for lunch. The lively conversation of three young Sisters as they washed clothes and sorted fruit into baskets to be taken to townspeople who were sick or lonely. As she stopped to really listen to these sounds, Mother Cabrini closed her eyes, breathed in the warm air, and silently prayed: *My God, if I could only extend my arms to embrace the world as a gift to you. Show me the way, and I will do everything with your help.*

Already, she had been able to expand beyond the convent—she had negotiated the purchase of a small school at Grumello. And with the help of her most educated Sisters, she established a teachers' college in Milan. Responding to the needs of neighboring villages, she set up foundations in the municipalities of Borghetto and Casalpusterlengo. All this with very little money. She was learning quickly how to negotiate, bargain, and beg.

For some men, the very sight of her habit created confusion. And in a pattern that would recur throughout Mother Cabrini's life, she encountered men who believed she must be naïve in dealing with money and tried to make her pay more than was called for in business transactions. Other men, intimidated by her nun's habit, feared the wrath of God if they tried to cheat her. She quickly became used to all these reactions and, guided by her innate frugality, made purchases for the least amount of money possible.

Monsignor Serrati was uneasy with the pace at which Mother Cabrini's new projects were being undertaken. At the end of one visit to the Codogno convent, he cautioned her. "You are simply moving too swiftly!" He and Mother Cabrini were sitting in the courtyard of the convent, out of earshot of the others on a warm afternoon, when he began to reprimand her. "I recognize that you want to help the children, but you are going to lose control if you have too many foundations to manage." He shook his head in disapproval. Mother Cabrini listened to her beloved friend and mentor. She did not want to upset this kind and generous man, but her sense of what she could accomplish was growing all the time. She waited a moment in the uncomfortable silence, then blurted out, "I want to open a house in Rome!" Serrati jerked his head up and stared at her in disbelief.

"Rome? This is foolishness! Your work is here, not in Rome," he said. "These are the people you need to help. No, I do not approve—I strongly recommend that you give up that notion."

Clearly rattled and upset with her, he rose, said goodbye quickly, and left.

Mother Cabrini did not follow him, but bowed her head to think. She could not go against him, yet her desire to grow was too strong to stop. And she sensed that her drive came from a source that was bigger than either of them. She decided to make plans to travel to Rome within the month.

It was an ambitious desire, but she wanted to meet Pope Leo XIII to ask for his approval of her Institute and also permission to establish a foundation in Rome. Finally, she wanted his blessing for her future missionary journeys. She knew this was a very big and daring request. She was, after all, still a country nun. But her childhood dream of going to China was still alive in her heart. Surely, he would see and appreciate the power of her determination.

She also needed allies. She only had several weeks in which to convince Serrati—as well Bishop Gelmini and others—to support her in this idea. And yet, unbeknownst to the determined young Mother Cabrini, a completely different purpose for her was soon to be revealed.

Chapter Six

THE PLIGHT OF ITALIAN IMMIGRANTS

"Before I say yes or no, *Madre*, I want to ask if you know what has been happening to some of our most impoverished citizens." Bishop Geremia Bonomelli was known as a practical, intelligent man who cared deeply for his congregation, and particularly for the poor. He was in charge of the diocese in which the Grumello school was situated. Now Mother Cabrini's meeting with him was taking an unexpected turn. She had come to visit in order to ask him to write a recommendation to the pope for her to open a foundation in Rome and she expected the meeting to be brief—either he would agree or he would not.

She sat before him in his small office with a tiny window that looked out on a courtyard filled with midday sunlight, and looked at him in surprise. "I am not sure what you mean…" she began.

"Men who cannot find work or food for their families are being lured into traveling by ship to other countries—for instance, America—in the hope of finding jobs that pay good money. But," he leaned forward to look directly at her, "we are hearing that once they arrive, either no jobs exist, or if they do find work, conditions are dangerous. These men live in desperate poverty and are taken advantage of by others who came before them. Not only do they have no money to send back to their families, but they cannot even feed themselves."

Mother Cabrini sat before him in a stiff wooden chair, unable to respond. She had heard that this was happening, but was not sure if it was true.

"In other countries, our people are ill-treated, they are hungry, become sick...and many are dying. As for whole families who travel to these other countries, they are subject to illness, and children are sometimes abandoned or orphaned. As a man of God, I cannot pretend I don't know this. I must do something—it might mean stopping them from getting on ships!" He was clearly angry and frustrated at the situation.

What was she to say? She had come selfishly to request a recommendation, but the situation he described spoke to her instantly. This was suffering, and these people very obviously needed help.

"Of course I will write your recommendation," the Bishop continued. "I know the work that you have done," he said. And now he looked directly into her eyes. "*Don't stop, keep going.* I hope you get your wish to expand to Rome. And if you do go there, I suggest you call on my friend Bishop Giovanni Battista Scalabrini. He can tell you more about the people who are leaving Italy today, tomorrow, maybe for years. He believes—as do I—that we need to provide real help before a large-scale calamity takes place."

Upon returning to her convent in Codogno, Mother Cabrini found letters from Monsignor Serrati and Bishop Gelmini. At last, they each gave their blessings for her to travel to Rome and to seek a meeting with the pope.

～

It would be a taxing trip, both physically and emotionally, so Mother Cabrini invited Sister Serafina Tommasi to join her. This new Sister to the convent was educated and well spoken, as well as physically much stronger than Mother Cabrini. They stopped first at the Church of the Gesu to pray at the altar of Saint Francis Xavier, where his arm is venerated as a relic.

I desire to travel to the missions in the Orient and I vow to find my way to China, as you told me to do so many years ago, prayed Mother Cabrini as she knelt before the altar.

But upon reaching the Vatican, it was Cardinal Lucido Maria Parocchi, not the pope, who met with the two women, and he did not hide his impatience with them. He listened, unsmilingly, as Mother Cabrini presented her requests.

"My dear, the timing is not right for your young Institute to open a house here in Rome," he said to the two nuns. "There are already many religious houses here doing the very work that you propose. Of course, teaching children is always a fine objective, but again, good schools already exist here that were founded many years ago."

Although the disappointment on the faces of Mother Cabrini and Sister Serafina was obvious, the Cardinal continued: "Furthermore, I must ask—what money do you have to start a convent or school here? I suspect that you have very little, if any money at all, for a foundation. I recommend that you both return to Codogno. The time is not right for your plan in Rome. Go back to your convent and gather more resources. Is the spirit strong in your Institute?"

Before Mother Cabrini could answer, Sister Serafina interrupted, saying, "It is very strong! We are missionaries! We already care for many orphans, and teach them as best we can.

More girls arrive every week who wish to join us. We perform all our spiritual practices with utmost dedication…"

Mother Cabrini raised her hand to stop Sister Serafina's passionate outburst. "We must take to heart the words of our venerable Cardinal," she said. "In truth, we do not know how strong the spirit is in our young Institute. We must consider this carefully, as he suggests."

The Cardinal noted the seriousness of the two women before him, and was pleased. "You have said that Our Lady of Grace is your Founder," he said to Mother Cabrini. "Then I wish for you to ask her to provide you with five hundred thousand lire. When that happens, I will recognize it as a sign of God's will that your Institute should open a foundation here in Rome."

The meeting had ended. Devastated, Mother Cabrini and Sister Serafina left his office. "He will change his mind, I know it," said Mother Cabrini. "I will attempt to see him again in a few weeks." Sister Serafina had her doubts, but she had already seen what Mother Cabrini's formidable will was able to accomplish and she knew that underestimating her was a mistake.

At the next meeting, Mother Cabrini noticed immediately that the Cardinal seemed less adamantly opposed to her plans. Had he read the letters of recommendation from her many friends? Now he asked her to describe her goals again in detail. This time, he seemed to listen more intently. At the end of their meeting, he told Mother Cabrini to wait another two weeks. How could they be patient? It was a trial, but in that time, Mother Cabrini and all the Sisters prayed for the answer to come that would allow them to grow and expand. And it did.

"Are you ready to obey?" the Cardinal asked her when the two met.

"Yes," she replied, looking directly into his eyes.

"Then I wish for you to found the house in Rome as you desire—and also a kindergarten outside of the city, in Aspra." She was not expecting this additional school—but Mother Cabrini gratefully accepted the Cardinal's statement. With a financial donation from Father Serrati, she found a place to rent in Rome and planned a trip to Aspra to do the same.

Though still impoverished, the Sisters rejoiced. It was the fall of 1887 and they would now, though they had little money, begin a foundation in Rome! But what would they sleep on? How would they buy furniture? Mother Cabrini went to public auctions to buy tables and chairs. The nuns found materials to make their own straw mattresses and purchased blankets from a small store.

In a few weeks, the nuns welcomed a visitor—Cardinal Parocchi himself came to see the new convent. Honored to be graced by his presence, the Sisters gave him a tour of their convent. He was delighted to see them and the bare beginnings of their foundation and promised that he would pray for their Institute, that it may thrive for many years to come.

Bishop Giovanni Battista Scalabrini of Piacenza strongly believed that unless he made his views known, the world would continue to ignore the terrible fate of Italian immigrants suffering in other countries. He was a professor and writer who often spoke out about social and political issues. In 1887, he published a pamphlet called *Italian Emigration in America* about poor Italian workers who sailed to America with the promise of a better life, only to face even worse conditions in the new land. Though he believed that emigration was right for all people, he railed at the exploitation of poor Italian workers in other countries.

At the suggestion of Bishop Bonomelli, Bishop Scalabrini and Mother Cabrini agreed to meet in Rome, in November 1887, soon after her foundation had been established there.

Neither looked forward to seeing the other—they both were busy and had much to do. But out of politeness, they finally agreed to meet at the Trevi Fountain. As soon as they spotted one another on a windy day at the fountain among the tourists, they greeted each other amiably and settled down in a café next to the gentle splashing of the fountain.

As soon as the pleasantries were over, Scalabrini launched into the shocking details of what happened to most of the poor Italian men and women who were arriving in America—rampant illness, malnourishment, filthy apartments shared by multiple families, orphaned children left to fend for themselves.

"I have sent some of my priests to establish foundations but much more help is needed for these Italians and their families there," he said, his dark eyes flashing with a mixture of anger, anxiety, and sadness. Something about him reminded Mother Cabrini of the missionary she had heard years ago standing on a box in Sant'Angelo. There was a great and critical need, Scalabrini was saying, a need for missionary work in this far-off land.

He made the case to her: "No one can stop people from emigrating—their lives were hard here, and they naturally wanted to seek out something better. So the answer is that the Catholic Church should be in these foreign cities to welcome and care for the Italian immigrants. Surely this is God's will!" he said. His eyes glittered intensely and Cabrini clearly understood the urgency of the situation he described.

"Tell me," she said to him. "Why do you not go there yourself?"

"I have more influence here in Italy," he said. "I have sent priests to New York, who have a small church from which they can help the poor. But I need to be in touch with Italians here who can influence religious and political men in America, who are in a position to provide help."

As the two walked through the narrow streets of Rome, they exchanged ideas about how to save the bodies and souls of their fellow countrymen. Surely education was imperative, but what about food and medicine? Someone had to appeal to the government, the church, even wealthy Italians, for help.

"There is no time to waste," Scalabrini said. "We have to do work as quickly as we can."

The meeting left Cabrini's mind swirling. Her heart had been set on China for so many years, but how could she ignore her own countrymen?

Archbishop Michael Augustine Corrigan of New York City knew all too well the dire needs of the newly arrived Italians to the city—he saw them with his own eyes every day on the very streets he walked. He read with interest Scalabrini's writings, and sent him a letter, begging for help. "We need good Italian priests," he wrote, "for the thousands of Italians arriving in New York City by ship."

Bishop Corrigan wrote that he was acquainted with a wealthy New Yorker named Mary Reid Cesnola, otherwise known as Countess Cesnola. She was absolutely determined to open a home for Italian children who had been orphaned in New York City, but she had no experience in this kind of project.

Could Bishop Scalabrini recommend someone? Scalabrini had just the person in mind; he just had to convince Mother Cabrini that America would be her next calling. It wasn't hard.

The more Cabrini learned about the conditions of the Italians in New York City, the more she felt the missionary call. Here was a clear and desperate need, and as Bishop Scalabrini said—how could she not heed this call? But what about her dream of China? Should this be abandoned? She admitted now that it was based on so little knowledge about that vast country, its people, and what their conditions really were. She could not even remember the names of the cities or provinces of China that she had learned in school.

To be called to save her own brothers and sisters of Italy—she could not ignore that. She had to go—but she could only do so if she had permission from Pope Leo XIII. She made a formal request to meet with him in December 1888. Then she set about conferring with her Sisters about what they really could do to help.

Pope Leo XIII was known as an advocate for education, the rights of working people and the poor, all of which strengthened the Catholic Church. So he was well aware of the great plight of emigrating Italians. Not only were they in physical danger, but they had lost touch with the Catholic Church in the absence of Italian priests and attended Protestant churches instead. Whole Italian families were now attending those churches—a catastrophe that Pope Leo wanted very much to halt.

And by now, he knew of the many accomplishments of Mother Cabrini. Her intelligence and leadership were becoming widely known. But unlike others who sought to rein in her ambition, Pope Leo XIII saw in Mother Cabrini an advocate like himself, and her potential to do great good for the world. He was seventy-eight when, in December of 1888, he agreed to meet with her and with three Sisters: Sister Maddalena Saverè, Sister Michelina Radice, and Sister Concetta Arnaboldi. White-haired and with a face that easily broke into a kind smile, Pope Leo XIII exuded a calm tranquility. He welcomed Mother Cabrini and the three Sisters into his chambers.

"Tell me, what is the purpose of your Institute?" he asked after they had all taken their seats.

"To grow in personal holiness and to do good for souls in every possible way, all over the world," replied Mother Cabrini. He noted her open, blue eyes and the way she looked directly into his, unafraid.

She and the Sisters sat in quiet awe of the pope and the elegance of the room itself, with its walls and ceiling painted with ornate frescoes.

"Do you have many members, novices?" he asked.

"Your Holiness, we number 105 Sisters," she answered. "In addition, there are forty novices and many others requesting entrance." Pope Leo's comforting, down-to-earth manner put Mother Cabrini at ease. She felt as if she had known him forever, as if he were a part of her family.

He was silent for a moment. She handed him a written paper expressing her love and readiness to undertake great works—and desire to cross the ocean to America. He thanked her, promising he would read it privately as soon as possible.

Several weeks later, Mother Cabrini was invited to see him again.

"Not to the East, but to the West," he said, in speaking of the direction of her missionary work, for it was not uncommon for missionaries to set out for Asia. "Your Institute is still young," he said to her. "It needs resources. Go to the United States. There you will find the means that will enable you to undertake a great field of work." She bowed her head deeply before him. How grateful she was to receive this blessing from the most important man in her life. Mother Cabrini was ready to embark on her first real missionary journey.

On March 19, 1889—the Feast of Saint Joseph—Mother Cabrini gathered with six Sisters at the convent in Codogno for a goodbye celebration. A simple meal had been prepared by the Sisters and friends from the town—fresh bread, cheese, fruit—and gifts were presented to the Sisters by men, women, and children. They sang songs and read poems. Bishop Scalabrini was in attendance, and gave a small wooden cross to each Missionary Sister bound for America. Bishop Serrati was there, and grasped Mother Cabrini's hands. "I do not know what to say to you," he said. "I leave you in the hands of God, and he will do with you what he wills."

The families of the departing Sisters came too, full of pride at their daughters' work ahead, and sorrow that the young women would be traveling so far away from home. Sister Concetta Arnaboldi laughed with her large family of sisters, brothers, cousins, aunts, and uncles as they stood close to her, and in their laughter at her silly jokes, they wiped away their tears. Sister Serafina's mother, an elegant woman who had never approved of her daughter's life as a nun, arrived with gifts for everyone. At last the small group boarded the train for Milan, and waved goodbye to their families and friends from the train windows. From Milan, they would travel to Paris and then to Le Havre, where their ship would be waiting.

On March 26, 1889, the steamboat *Bourgogne*, with Cabrini and six young Missionary Sisters, as well as 1,500 Italian emigrants on board, set off across the Atlantic. It was not an easy voyage.

Chapter Seven

NOT WELCOME IN NEW YORK

A chilly wind blew around the black skirts of the nun as she knocked five, six, seven times before the heavy door finally opened. "*Buongiorno*," said the nun to the man dressed in a black cassock who stood in the doorway of the Saint Joachim Church rectory on Twenty-Six Roosevelt Street in New York City.

"We have just arrived…*l'arcivescovo ha richiesto d' incontrarmi*…Bishop Scalabrini arranged for us to come here!"

Though her face was pale, her warm blue eyes glittered with eager excitement as she introduced herself as Mother Frances Xavier Cabrini, saying the English version of her name. The man did not smile, but tilted his head slightly. "*Mi pardone*, we were not expecting you. Please come in."

Mother Cabrini stepped over the threshold and the man's eyes widened when he saw six young Sisters behind her. They clung to large unwieldy bags as they dutifully marched up the steps and into the foyer, away from the clatter of Lower Manhattan—fruit vendors calling out, children shouting, horses clip-clopping by.

The young nuns looked around the cool interior of the rectory. Though their faces showed signs of fatigue, they were curious and alert. "May I introduce Sister Serafina Tommasi," said Mother Cabrini, "and Sister Garbriella Lunati…" The priest nodded at these introductions, and then put up his hand.

"*Madre Cabrini*, please follow me," interrupted the man as he turned away from the group. Mother Cabrini followed, looking back over her shoulder at the young nuns signaling with her eyes, *I will be back soon!*

She stood before three priests. "Thank you for receiving us!" she said. "We are here finally after a long journey…As you know, from Italy Bishop Scalabrini has been in touch with Archbishop Corrigan here in New York, who requested that we come here to open an orphanage and teach and do God's work for our poor country people. If you could please show us our rooms, many of my daughters were quite ill on our sea voyage and are in great need of rest."

The men shifted uncomfortably, and for several moments did not speak. Mother Cabrini's questioning gaze moved from one to the other. "You see, we have no place for you," one of them said finally. "We have no place for you to stay, no food, and…no money. Conditions are very hard here in New York City."

Mother Cabrini listened and was quiet. Her expression showed no disappointment, but a flicker of resolve crossed her eyes. "Can you direct me to lodging nearby…of any kind?"

It was 1889. What Mother Cabrini had only glimpsed in the distance they had walked from the boat dock and Twenty-Six Roosevelt Street—the crowded streets filled with voices speaking many languages—was a fraction of the immigrant population that had entered New York City and other cities on the east coast of the country in the previous decade. In 1889 alone, more that 349,000 immigrants had arrived at Castle Garden in Lower Manhattan.

Thousands of Italians, particularly from southern Sicily and Sardinia, were boarding steam ships for America. Some sought to escape the poverty of their homeland, some were fugitives from justice, and some had been lured by "agents," who for a fee had guaranteed them jobs in America. New York, Boston, and other American cities were flooded with the immigrants, their numbers swelling to millions. The jobs the men got were dangerous—working in sewers, digging tunnels—and a big portion of their small wages went to the rent of crowded tenements, and to *padrones* as payback for getting them a job.

The tenements in the Lower East Side of Manhattan, single-family dwellings that had been divided into smaller rooms, were squalid, cramped spaces with ten or twenty families often sharing one toilet. Children had no school to go to, and when diseases such as measles and influenza spread quickly, thousands became orphaned and were left to beg for food. Charity organizations were springing up in a desperate attempt to save abandoned babies and children from harm or even death. The only room the Scalabrinian priests could locate for Mother Cabrini and the Sisters was in one such tenement.

A bed at last! thought Mother Cabrini. *And one that doesn't rock upon high ocean waves.* The young nuns climbed the stairs and reached their room, exhausted. Upon opening the door, they gasped at the foul smell emanating from the trash that was scattered on the floor, and the sight of scurrying cockroaches. "*Mio dio!*" cried Sister Serafina. "I cannot sleep here!"

"We will take turns sleeping," said Mother Cabrini, trying to remain calm and counter the mounting distress among the Sisters. But she wondered, *What have we come to?* Sister Concetta Arnaboldi, just twenty-one years old, covered her face with her hands and burst into tears.

~

Mother Cabrini spread out her coat and sat on it, leaning against the wall. But she could hardly rest—her mind actively reviewed all she had seen and heard. She prayed: *Jesus, light the path before me, give us strength and courage to find a place to stay…to do your will…*She was thirty-eight years old. This was her first real mission but when she'd envisioned it in Codogno, she had not foreseen these gritty streets, the stink, or the hungry looks on the faces of so many children. She stared into the dark, shadowy room. Some of the sisters slept fitfully; others, she knew, were wide awake.

Italia, with its clean air and light open spaces, seemed like another world. But Jesus was her spouse, and he had called her here to this wretched place for a reason. She closed her eyes and listened. She could hear voices arguing in other rooms of the building, and on the street below a drunken man raged alone. Missionary work was what she longed to do her entire life. It would not be easy, she was aware of that. Those dirty, hungry people, those little children with sad, frightened faces—she would find a way to bring them relief, the comfort and guidance of their religion, as well as food, education, medicine if they needed it too—but how? With what resources? She realized how massively unprepared she and her Sisters were for this kind of hardship.

God is all-powerful, and so I can endure.

There was much to be done. To do real work here, she would need many more Sisters to join them from Italy. She would also need the help and blessing of Archbishop Corrigan.

~

Mother Cabrini sat before the Archbishop in his New York office. A gray light streamed into the large, cold room. It was a cold March day—Mother Cabrini and her Sisters had arrived in New York City a few days before, to no welcome at all. Now the meeting with Corrigan was not going well.

Bishop Corrigan's expression was stern and tight. "You and your Missionary Sisters should not—cannot—stay in New York," he said in a low, even voice. "There is no money, first of all, to pay for your care here. The Countess Cesnola may want to open her orphanage on East Fifty-Ninth Street, but this is impossible! The residents of that neighborhood would not stand for having such as establishment in their midst!" he almost shouted. "And furthermore, she has not raised enough money for it."

Cabrini fixed her blue eyes on Corrigan, but did not speak. She was tired. The sea voyage had traumatized her and the other Sisters. In the first days on the water, a storm had pounded the steam ship *Bourgogne*, dangerously tossing it about on high waves. Waves that rose like mountains lifted the ship up and then suddenly dropped it down at a terrifying angle. The ship had rocked from side to side, then was lifted up again so quickly that the Sisters thought it would surely capsize. Seasick and terrified, they all prayed constantly.

Yet even when the sea calmed, the cabins were airless and stinking. Finally, after twelve days of illness and desolation, the *Bourgogne* passengers caught sight of the Statue of Liberty—a gift from the French government just three years earlier—and rejoiced. A doctor came on board to check each passenger's health, and only after he had given his permission were they then allowed to disembark, many of them running from the boat, giddy to be free of it.

∼

Archbishop Michael Corrigan, who was born of Irish parents in Newark, New Jersey, was not afraid of confrontation. He was well educated, had traveled in Europe, and had recently overseen the completion of Saint Patrick's Cathedral—a major undertaking of which he was especially proud. He was a conservative and cautious man who was careful with his power to influence. For this reason, he would not give his blessing to a project that could anger some of the richest residents in New York.

Mother Cabrini sat upright in the chair in front of his desk. There was so much she could say right now, but chose not to. She would not mention the stiff greeting she had received from the Scalabrinian Brothers or the dirty, cockroach-infested room that they had found late at night for her and her Sisters to stay.

Thankfully, they'd been saved by the kindness of the Sisters of Charity who heard of their arrival in New York and invited them to stay at their convent for several weeks. Having opened the Foundling Asylum on Sixty-Eighth Street, these Sisters knew very well that Mother Cabrini and her group might be able to save more lost children. No, she would not compare the welcome she'd received from the Sisters of Charity to the cold welcome she was receiving from the Archbishop.

And she didn't want to speak about the grim scenes she'd already witnessed—men and women picking through garbage, wearing dirt-caked, threadbare clothes. Her heart hurt especially for the children, the street urchins she had seen begging for food during the day, and curled up in doorway corners at night. Was there no one who cared for them? Some were obviously sick and most appeared to be malnourished.

This is what Bishop Scalabrini had warned her about: Conditions were so bad that the bodies of babies were sometimes found on the streets. Thankfully, she had not seen that. But she had seen children barely six years old acting as caretakers to their baby siblings, with no parent in sight. A few of the younger Sisters cried at these scenes, but Mother Cabrini could feel her determination deepen. These were her countrymen, good people, yet they'd fallen into a degrading, hopeless life here, completely unmoored from the faith and traditions that in the Italian villages had kept them safe.

No, she wasn't going to say any of this to a man who appeared to be in a hurry for her to leave. This conversation was over. Mother Cabrini nodded her head, and quietly got up and left. She knew her next step—she would find her way to the door of Countess Cesnola.

Chapter Eight

THE COUNTESS AND THE ORPHANAGE

"Do come in!" Mary di Cesnola greeted Mother Cabrini and Sister Serafina in the foyer of her Fifty-Seventh Street townhouse, in one of the wealthiest neighborhoods of New York City. "An unexpected surprise—I am very pleased to meet you at last!" The Countess Cesnola's eyes glittered with excitement as she ushered the petite Mother Cabrini and Sister Serafina down a long hallway into the sitting room.

Sunlight shone through the tall windows onto the deep green and blue Turkish carpet. The Countess indicated that the two nuns should sit on finely embroidered chairs, her eyes flickering quickly over their worn clothing and scuffed shoes. Assessment went the other way too. The eyes of Mother Cabrini and Sister Serafina darted about the luxuriously furnished room, the Countess's fine silk dress and gold rings, taking in the dark patterned wallpaper and the elegant furniture.

A servant in a crisply ironed uniform stepped into the room, carrying a silver tray with a silver teapot and three delicate teacups, and a small plate of biscuits. She set it on a polished wood table between the women.

"Thank you for your kindness in allowing us to visit," began Mother Cabrini in Italian as Sister Serafina translated to the Countess. "I felt I must come to speak with you directly," said Mother Cabrini, "about the need for an orphanage…"

"Of course, of course, yes!" interrupted the Countess, waving her arms. "I have spoken at length to the Archbishop about this—I refuse to accept his objections. As I wrote to you, I have the funds to sustain a location for these children on Fifty-Ninth Street, just around the corner. I am at a loss as to why he can't see the urgency of this!"

Mother Cabrini studied the Countess—an unusual woman. She seemed somewhat excitable, but was she a woman of faith? She had two daughters of her own, but where did this desire to help orphans originate?

She might not have any business sense at all, thought Mother Cabrini, *but surely she has access to far more than just the $5,000 she has raised for this orphanage. If the passions of this woman are genuine and true, she could fund many projects for the Italian immigrants who live in utter destitution less than five miles away.*

With Sister Serafina translating, the two women shared their ideas for the orphanage. "We must teach them a catechism, begin a children's Bible study."

"They must have many books, and clean clothes…"

"My cook knows a woman who can prepare meals for them!" They both grew more excited the more they talked and envisioned ways to rescue the lives and souls of poor, abandoned Italian children. Countess Cesnola thrilled at having the two nuns before her. In Mother Cabrini she found the very person who could advance her wish to establish an orphanage. It would be an advantage, in many ways, to have this nun on her side. The Countess was on a personal campaign to improve the image of her husband, and an orphanage run by Mother Cabrini could boost his image considerably.

Countess Cesnola came from the finest American stock. Born Mary Jennings Reid, she was the daughter of Captain Samuel Chester Reid, a hero in the War of 1812. Her husband, Luigi Palma di Cesnola, was a Piedmontese Count who served in the Sardinian army and then emigrated to America in 1858. The two were married in 1861 and Cesnola served as colonel in the Civil War, earning a medal of honor. He then served as the United States consul in Cyprus, where he organized excavations that unearthed valuable antiquities—an activity that many Cypriots considered stealing. Di Cesnola sold about twenty-two thousand of these pieces to the Metropolitan Museum of Art, and he was appointed the museum's first director in 1879.

Not everyone appreciated the way Cesnola excavated these antiquities or his tendency to boast about their worth—the word *looting* was whispered behind his back. Many people wondered: Was Count Cesnola really the man of high morals that he claimed to be? This is why Countess Cesnola felt that their reputation might be greatly improved by associating with Mother Cabrini in this charitable work.

Mary di Cesnola could not have been more different from Mother Cabrini. She was rich and moved among the most privileged circles of New York City society. Yet the two women shared a mutual goal: to help poor, abandoned Italian children. "Why don't we pay a visit to Archbishop Corrigan tomorrow—together?" suggested the Countess with a gleam in her eye. "I am sure we can convince him to let us establish our orphanage."

~

Appalled at their boldness, Corrigan glared at the two women who came to sit before him, his face reddening with anger. How dare they question his decision? He'd already expressed his feelings about this orphanage. He was not about to back down, even under that intense gaze of Mother Cabrini's blue eyes.

"My suggestion, Mother Cabrini, is that you take your Sisters and go back to Italy on the next boat!" he burst out.

Mother Cabrini's even expression did not change. "I was sent here by Pope Leo XIII," she said, "and therefore I will stay." The women departed his office—Mother Cabrini walking slowly, as if ill—and as he watched them go, Corrigan recognized that he'd just encountered an extraordinary stubborn strength in this nun from Italy. She was bold, and unmoved by his authority. Though she was clearly physically infirm, he sensed Cabrini was not about to give up.

Alone in his office, he admitted to himself that New York's Italian immigrants desperately needed someone like her. The abandoned children and adults who spoke no English—most were uneducated and had nowhere to turn to for food or shelter, a shameful situation. He suspected this was not the last he would see of Mother Cabrini.

The Sisters had only been in New York City for a few weeks, and already had accomplished much, though their own conditions were dire. They worked for the Scalabrinian Brothers as teachers at their Saint Joachim School located in the heart of the city's most infamously poor neighborhood called the Five Points section of Lower Manhattan. They had no books or other supplies for the children, and the Brothers had no money pay the nuns, and could not even offer them a place to live, except for a brothel nearby. In spite of all this, Mother Cabrini and her Sisters agreed to teach in the school, and find a way to make it their convent.

It was appalling how these and other men of faith were so unwilling to help in the efforts to care for and teach the poorest children right in their own neighborhood. Archbishop Corrigan, who soon realized she was not returning to Italy as he had ordered, told Mother Cabrini that if she wanted to raise money she was to go only to other Italians. The Scalabrinian Brothers also refused to help locate a suitable house for her and her Sisters to live, and only did so when Mother Cabrini wrote a letter of complaint to Bishop Scalabrini in Italy.

To raise money, she and Sister Serafina paid a visit to the Father Superior of the Franciscans and also the Superior of the Jesuits—and both refused to help. "How could they not help?" cried Sister Serafina as the two women walked down Broadway, heading back to Saint Joachim Church after being denied help. The sidewalks were full of people strolling or stopping into small stores, or at vendors' carts propped up on the curbs. Above the street, the iron fire escapes on the buildings' facades were draped with mattresses, pillows, and laundry being aired out.

The two nuns in their worn black habits stood out in the crowd and drew stares from people as they passed. "How could they not see the great need all around this city, and how much we could do even with a small amount of money?" said Sister Serafina, now quite angry.

"Money is scarce," responded Mother Cabrini. "But perhaps they believe we are not established enough yet. And perhaps they think we are trying to take something from them—a pride in their own work for the poor. But let's not dwell on what they don't give us, but put our attention on what we can do ourselves."

Mother Cabrini marveled at the lively street scene. Never before had she seen so many nationalities mingling together in a crowd. She was surprised to discover seven Protestant churches and a Jewish temple near their humble convent. "Would that I had the wealth to buy all of them," she wrote to Mother Savarè, a dear friend who managed the Missionary Sisters of the Sacred Heart convent in Rome, "and turn them over to our most holy religion."

In her prayers, Mother Cabrini asked for courage and ability to find funds. *Show me where to find the money to do the work you want us to do!*

Her prayers were answered: Help came from *women* of faith. Sister Mary Irene, Superior of the Sisters of Charity in New York City gave a gold piece to Mother Cabrini for her new school. A few months later, she gave her twenty dollars, then five dollars, candelabras, two vases, two vestments for Mass, an altar cloth, and a vigil light. Later she donated twenty-two iron beds. The Bon Secours Sisters donated furniture for the new orphanage. The Madames of the Sacred Heart donated linens for children's beds. The French Sisters of Charity promised to speak well of the Italian missionaries to the influential people of their community—and urge them to donate money.

Mother Cabrini and her Sisters were deeply grateful. "My only regret is that I cannot express my gratitude to them because I speak only Italian and they understand only English," said Mother Cabrini to Sister Ricci one evening when the Sisters had gathered for a meager dinner. They were speaking about the many things they needed, especially now that word was spreading that the Missionary Sisters of the Sacred Heart had established a convent in tenement rooms in the Five Points section.

"Opening the door today was like opening a cage full of birds," commented one Sister. "A hundred children came fluttering in."

"What did they want?" asked another.

"They went into the garden to play, and they asked for food."

Mother Cabrini smiled at hearing this.

"This is wonderful," she said. "Let us help welcome them at the upcoming Feast Days here at the church. My hope is that *all* children and families will come to eat and enjoy themselves, and remember the Feast Days from home."

"A lot of the men have already returned to Italy," said another. "Some of them seem to go back and forth."

"Yes, but for those who have chosen to remain, or who brought their families here, they're the ones who need our help to adapt to a new life, but also to remember where they came from," said Mother Cabrini.

Then she sat back on the bench to reflect. Really helping these immigrants in the long term would be a challenge unlike any she—or perhaps anyone—had ever undertaken. Two countries, two languages—so much help was needed for immigrants, and somehow she and the Sisters had to adapt to this new place as quickly as possible. How could she and her Sisters offer lasting help to the generations of Italians who would arrive here to live? And how could she get others to see how important it was to provide financial help? She needed more Sisters to be here in America, she realized. And they needed to become American themselves.

Chapter Nine

MISSIONARY LIFE IN THE SLUMS

Count Luigi Palma di Cesnola always enjoyed coming home to find the Sisters visiting his wife. They were Italian, of course, but also highly intelligent and delightful conversationalists. Sister Serafina Tommasi, the most educated of all the Missionary Sisters of the Sacred Heart, spoke perfect English as well as French and German. At Mother Cabrini's request, she gave the others English lessons whenever they had the time. Lively and fun, she was a good teacher, always encouraging her Sisters to practice speaking English with each other as often as possible.

Today she and Mother Cabrini were both visiting his wife, talking about how to raise funds for the orphanage and for school supplies. Countess Cesnola was happy to report to Mother Cabrini that she had coaxed her husband into making a list of the names and addresses of all the wealthy members of the Metropolitan Museum. Just as the Count entered the sitting room, his wife was going over the list with the two nuns.

"And you have my permission to use my name whenever you call on these men," boomed the Count, surprising the women. "I hope they are generous!" He took the list and ceremoniously handed it to Sister Serafina. "May you raise all the funds you need for the orphanage and many other projects in the future."

Later that evening, Mother Cabrini and Sister Serafina excitedly showed the list to the other Sisters at dinner. "I intend to visit every single man on his list—one by one—starting tomorrow," exclaimed Mother Cabrini.

The Sisters were ecstatic. Begging on the street and selling their embroidery and other handicrafts at the market never produced much money, and they badly needed pencils and paper for their little school. Whenever they had extra money, they bought food for themselves. And yet, not one of them complained—they took the hardship and deprivation very much in stride as part of the missionary life. And something else: Their obvious poverty made it easier for poor people to approach them for help.

The next day, Mother Cabrini received another piece of good news: Archbishop Corrigan decided to allow the orphanage to open on Fifty-Ninth Street after all. Mother Cabrini hurried uptown to visit Countess Cesnola. The Countess clapped her hands with joy when Mother Cabrini showed her his note.

"I know just the rooms that we will rent—immediately!" She fluttered around her sitting room while planning their next steps. "These rooms are right around the corner on Fifty-Ninth Street. They're not big, but we can fill them with as many children as possible! I'm going to speak to my cook right away so she can prepare food, and of course we need to get beds in there…"

Mother Cabrini watched in fascination as the Countess happily chattered—she seemed almost possessed with the thrill of doing such good. Two weeks later, on the chilly Sunday of April 21, 1889, the two women officially opened the orphanage. Archbishop Corrigan arrived in the afternoon and greeted the Countess and Mother Cabrini graciously, while the Sisters showed some of the children around their new rooms.

A tall young man approached Mother Cabrini and introduced himself as a reporter from *The Sun*, a widely read city newspaper. "May I ask you some questions about your hopes for this establishment?" he asked. Mother Cabrini quickly called for Sister Serafina to come to her aid for translation.

After listening to the young man explain that he wanted to write a story for one of the city's most prominent newspapers about her efforts to help Italian children, Mother Cabrini stared at him, speechless. Was he an angel sent from Heaven? Such a story would reach thousands of New Yorkers—some of whom might be moved to donate money! She quickly guided him and Sister Serafina to a small garden table at the rear of the townhouse, where they could all sit.

"What is your goal for this little orphanage?" he asked, turning to Sister Serafina to translate. He was struck by the intelligence and charm of Sister Serafina, and his eyes lingered on hers for just a moment as she translated. What beautiful dark eyes she had, and how merry she seemed! "Our object is to rescue the Italian orphans of the city from the misery and dangers that threaten them and to make good men and women of them," replied Mother Cabrini when Sister Serafina translated his question. "At present, we are especially anxious about the Italian girls who have no decent homes, but later on we shall look out for the boys also."

"What happened to the parents of these children?" asked the reporter.

"Their parents, who have come here expecting to be rich immediately, now learn their mistake, and being short of money, they set the children adrift to care for themselves," said Cabrini.

"Then, too, there are many poor Italians who are barely able to supply food for the numerous mouths dependent upon them, and they are glad to let us take some of their children and bring them up properly."

The reporter took notes as fast as he could, then looked up at Mother Cabrini. "How did you find these children?" He could not help but stare a bit at Sister Serafina. Her skin was creamy white. How could this beauty be a nun?

"Our mode of work is to go right down into the Italian quarters and go from house to house, from apartment to apartment," said Mother Cabrini, who noticed the reporter's distracted air but forged ahead with her explanation.

"Do they welcome you, or are they suspicious?" he asked.

"We are recognized by all Italians, and many of them are glad to see us," explained Mother Cabrini. "We try to learn about all the Italian children we meet, whether they have proper homes and proper schooling."

"Why do you place attention so much on helping girls?"

"The temptations that a big city like this offers to poor, ignorant girls of any nationality are very great, and to abandoned Italian girls, who have no means of livelihood and are ignorant, even of the language of those around them, they are terrible."

The reporter thanked Sister Serafina and Mother Cabrini, then asked if they might give him a short tour of the children's rooms. Having just heard the scope of their goals, the reporter was surprised to see how small the rooms were. The beds were squeezed tightly together, leaving little space for playing. Not wanting to be disrespectful, he said nothing, but Mother Cabrini caught his reaction and quickly explained, "As soon as our means allow, we intend to have a larger house, where we can accommodate all the children that come to us."

Yes, a small orphanage had been established, but this was just the bare beginning of what she wanted to do. She watched as the reporter said goodbye—did she catch a slight look of longing in his glance at Sister Serafina? She smiled and hoped he would write a story that would change how people perceived Italians in this cruel city.

While walking back along the windswept sidewalks to the convent that evening with Sister Serafina, Mother Cabrini was struck by the stark differences between the lives of the rich and the lives of the poor. They lived so close in New York—really just a few miles apart—but it was as if they were in separate cities. On Fifty-Ninth Street, well-dressed families strolled along clean sidewalks, their children well-fed and cheerful.

By the time she reached White Street in Lower Manhattan, where the Sisters had found rooms for their tiny convent, Mother Cabrini observed that most people wore old, tattered clothing, and children could be seen wandering about with no adult looking after them. Some had dirty hands and faces, and their eyes darted around with fear.

Every day, Mother Cabrini and her Sisters tried to make sense of these vast disparities and of how dangerous the poor neighborhoods were. Irish, Polish, Black, Jewish, Christian… so many languages could be heard as people pushed shoulder to shoulder along the sidewalks, so crowded that the Sisters had to link arms not to lose one another. From their beds at night, they were sometimes awakened by raucous laughing and fighting on the street.

In the daytime, they witnessed men and women cruelly taunt people from countries not their own, and cried with anxiety when fist fights between complete strangers, seemingly triggered by petty slights, broke out in front of them on the street. Dark-skinned southern Italians seemed to be the target of constant name-calling and abuse. But when they gathered in the evening in their small convent, the Sisters created their own little oasis of calm and joy.

Sister Serafina read stories out loud from the daily newspapers in an effort to help them all understand their new world. They were aggrieved at how often Italian immigrants were described as violent and vindictive. The immigrants the Sisters had come to know in Five Points were mostly garbage pickers. Yes, some committed crimes, but poverty had pushed a lot of them into it. Men who were lucky enough to find work were often injured at those jobs and so lost them, and dying from untreated wounds was not uncommon.

And even for men who did have jobs, swindlers waited around every corner, ready to trick them out of their wages. Some of the coldest treatment came from the Irish who, having immigrated to New York just years before to escape the potato famine in their country, resented the new influx of Italian immigrants who were willing work for lower wages and longer hours just to avoid starvation. Many Irish saw the Italian devotion to saints as being a kind of strange superstition.

At the end of each day, the Sisters lit candles, prayed, and then shared what little food they had for dinner. One evening, Sister Margherita Ramelli was uncharacteristically quiet, her face drawn and forlorn. Finally, she broke her silence: "The new baby in the Canese family died," she blurted out. "I was there this afternoon when she died in her mama's arms."

Sister Ramelli began to cry. "The other children are sick too," she said. "It might be typhoid. It's so awful there—four families all living together—it's filthy and the only window is stuck shut. All the children were there and saw the baby die. Their mama cried and cried. Do you remember—their papa died last month, crushed in an accident working in the tunnel."

The Sisters put their arms around Sister Ramelli. Some wept with her. Mother Cabrini said, "We will pray for the family tonight and visit them early tomorrow. Perhaps some of the children can come here to have some room to play and move about. We must find a doctor who can visit the family." For a long time the women were silent, overcome by sadness.

Sister Umelia Capietti finally spoke. "Two young Irish girls arrived at our doorstep today, asking to join the Missionary Sisters of the Sacred Heart. Their names are Loretta Garvey and Elizabeth Desmond." The other Sisters were keenly interested and asked about the girls. "Well, I know they're Irish, but I'm not sure if they were born in Ireland or America," said Sister Capietti, "but they want to join us as postulants! They'll be coming back here tomorrow, *Madre*."

Sister Serafina also had some news. "I saw something quite fascinating today," she said. "I was on my way to visit the Rossini family—their children are also sick—and I discovered that today, April 30, is the one-hundredth anniversary of the inauguration of America's first president, George Washington!"

Mother Cabrini and the other Sisters listened in rapt attention. "There was a big celebration—and President Benjamin Harrison apparently decided to follow the path of that first inauguration by taking a boat from New Jersey to Wall Street in southern Manhattan, then to Saint Paul's Church and on into the city. I suddenly found that streets I needed to cross were blocked off."

Sister Serafina's eyes lit up as she described the parade, waving her hands in the air to demonstrate how big it was. "There must have been hundreds of people, all dressed in fine clothing," she said, "walking along with banners of city clubs, and there were marching bands and loud music. And ships, big ones and small ones, were all bumping against one another in the water nearby, sounding their horns—it was magnificent! I wish you all had been with me so that you could have seen it too."

As the Sisters chimed in with questions, Mother Cabrini reflected, *Ah, now I understand why all the wealthy people I tried to visit to solicit money were not at home or were too busy to see me, even though I told them Count di Cesnola had sent me.* Later that night, thinking of all that she'd heard, Mother Cabrini felt acutely how she and the Sisters—and all Italian immigrants—were outsiders looking in. Even when they had visited Saint Patrick's Cathedral the week before, she and the Sisters felt alienated by the custom that required payment to enter.

Other parishioners stared at her when she sat down in a pew, then they turned away from her with looks of disgust. Archbishop Corrigan insisted that she raise funds only from Italians, and yet most Italians who could afford to make a donation seemed reluctant to do so. *There is so much wealth here*, prayed Mother Cabrini that night to her Savior Jesus. *Yet it all seems out of my reach. Give me the courage to find ways to do the work you have sent me to do for my beloved people, who are so poor.*

As she closed her eyes to sleep, she felt hopeless, so she continued to pray. *Give me strength, Jesus, to keep serving my people.* Her hopelessness began to dissipate, and in its place she sensed a determination. Suddenly, she awoke and rose, and went to her desk. She knew what had to be done: More women must join them here in America to accomplish all that she had in mind. And she needed a bigger space in which to house abandoned children. Surely she could find a place somewhere. Perhaps she could ask Archbishop Corrigan to help her locate a new building. She sat down and wrote him a letter at once, after which she began to plan a return to Italy—she would take the two Irish girls with her so that they could officially join her order. Another solution was to find more young American women who could join them here.

In July, Mother Cabrini returned by ship to Le Havre. This was her second sea journey, and it was no easier than the first. But now she knew not to take a calm sea for granted—it could be overtaken by a violent storm at any time. And when frighteningly bad weather tossed the boat, she now knew it would not last forever.

When they finally arrived safely in Codogno, she and the young Irish women were warmly welcomed by her Sisters. Mother Cabrini relaxed at the very sight of the town, and her "Daughters" who came to greet her. The bustling convent was her home and anchor, and she slept well. That night, she dreamed that she was walking along a road near the village of Sant'Angelo, where she was born. Eager to reach home, she was impatient that the road seemed to continually unwind before her, making her journey longer and longer.

Finally, she turned a corner and before her stood a large country house that had never been there before, perched on a grassy cliff overlooking a wide river. She began to approach, drawn to it as if this was her true home. The air was clear and fresh, birds darted from tree to tree against the blue sky. The front door opened and…suddenly she awoke. Confused for a moment, Mother Cabrini stared into the dim morning light of her room. She was in Codogno, but her heart felt as if she had been somewhere else. She rose, shaking off the strange sensation, and began to pray. Her task for the day was to determine which Sisters would be ready to return with her to America.

In the following days, she spoke privately to each of the Sisters in Codogno, the ones she knew quite well, and the women who had joined since she had been in America; most of them were eager to return to America with her.

She was delighted when Monsignor Serrati visited one afternoon, and she welcomed him into the courtyard where the sun was shining hotly. They sat together in the same spot where they had met when Serrati vehemently admonished her not to go to Rome. Now Mother Cabrini told him about her sea voyages, and described the tall buildings of New York City, the slums that existed just blocks from the richest neighborhoods, and how the Sisters had been working as teachers in the tiny school, about the immigrants in crowded tenement buildings, and the desperate need for food, education, and a connection to the Church.

As Seratti listened to his friend recount her adventures, he observed how much she had grown in just four months. She was confident and more animated than he had ever seen her. Her calling as a missionary, he saw, was at last realized. Although she was almost forty, and still physically weak at times, she had a new fire in her blue eyes, and determination in her voice.

"As soon as I can," she said, "I need to go again to Rome, to ask for money to expand all our missionary work," she said. Serrati smiled—she was a fearless, spirited woman whose faith was very possibly stronger than his own. And to think that he had once tried to hold her back!

Mother Cabrini was often restless. Her mind and her body always seemed to be several steps ahead of everyone else. Her dreams for schools and orphanages were big—and were always impossible financially—but that did not stop her from constantly plotting ways to make them possible. A month later she traveled to Rome, first to visit her friend and confidante, Mother Maddalena Savarè, who managed the convent there. After that, she made arrangements to go to the Vatican.

And now, once again, she found herself being led into Pope Leo's quiet office chamber. Bowing her head, she sat before the old man and told him about the harsh poverty of Italians in America, how they lived in filthy, crowded tenements that made them sick, that medical help was badly needed, that Italians were subject to derision and insults, and so many had lost touch with their Catholic faith.

Pope Leo listened to every word without interrupting—he wanted to hear it all—not only about America, but how fiercely Mother Cabrini desired to help, and her ideas about the best ways to do so. Before him was the soul of a missionary and he would help her do the work of the Church.

Chapter Ten

A PLACE IN THE COUNTRY FOR CHILDREN

Mother Cabrini held two letters. Sitting in her room in Codogno, she studied the handwriting on each envelope. One was from Sister Bernardina Valisneri in New York—she opened that one first. Archbishop Corrigan had been asking the Sisters when Mother Cabrini was to return, wrote Sister Bernardina—he had exciting news.

The Jesuits, who had so quickly turned down Mother Cabrini's first request for financial help, now had an offer: She and the Missionary Sisters of the Sacred Heart could purchase their 450-acre property—at a reduced price—near Poughkeepsie, New York, if she so wished. There was a villa, barns, and some farm animals too!

La Madre smiled—this sounded promising. She had prayed for more space in which to care for orphans in New York, but never dreamed of such a location outside the city. She closed her eyes for a moment and imagined how wonderful it would be for children who had known only life in the slums to live in the country. The second letter came from Milan. She opened it carefully, and her eyes filled with tears as she read:

"My dear *Madre Cabrini*, I regret that I must share with you the news that our daughter Serafina Tommasi has died. She was devoted to you and traveling with you, and the Missionary Sisters of the Sacred Heart to New York was the fulfillment of her dreams. As you know, she had come home to us just early this year, complaining of feeling ill, but the doctor was not able to help her. She was just thirty-two. I hope that you know that she died with joy in her heart at having done the missionary work that she wanted so much to do, above all else."

Mother Cabrini folded the letter from Sister Serafina's mother twice and placed it on the table near her chair, as if to close out the news it carried. She looked out at children playing in the courtyard, stunned by this sudden big loss. The scene outside looked sharper, brighter.

What a good friend Sister Serafina had been! Her joyful spirit had lightened their despair in the first months in New York, when so much seemed to be against them. Quick and intelligent, she had been one of the most enthusiastic Sisters among that first small group. And she had taught them all English, which helped them each in finding their way around the strange new city. And now—gone, just like that.

Mother Cabrini closed her eyes and prayed for Sister Serafina's soul. The young woman had come from a well-educated and affluent family, yet she had independently taken a different path in joining the Missionary Sisters. And now there was no chance for Mother Cabrini to tell her friend how much she appreciated all that she had given up and done. She thought of Sister Serafina in Heaven with her loving spouse, and this gave Mother Cabrini comfort.

~

Back in New York in April, Mother Cabrini brought with her seven young Sisters from Italy who were filled with a fervent missionary spirit and were eager to join the others in New York. By now Mother Cabrini had crossed the ocean more times than most people would in their whole lives. To her, the sea voyages served as respites from the constant activity of her life. On the long days on ships crossing the ocean, she could relax and study the sea and sky, meditating on the wonders of nature. While most passengers became seasick or confined themselves to their cabins in terror when storms arose, Mother Cabrini stayed on deck as much as possible for the air.

She had learned to focus on the horizon to quell seasickness—and it worked. Still, from time to time she "paid the tribute that the fish demand," as she slyly called being ill over the rails. Sea voyages gave Mother Cabrini time to reflect on her wishes for her beloved Sisters, now living in many parts of the world. She sent them long letters, which were picked up by passing boats. She asked the Sisters to copy them and send them on to Sisters in all other houses.

Confronted with spectacular natural scenes that moved her deeply, she tried to put into words what she saw:

"I write to you after having witnessed a spectacle most novel for me as well as for the crew," she wrote on April 24, 1890. "Toward eleven we saw ourselves surrounded by icebergs on every part of the horizon. At first they seemed inconsequential masses, but as some drew closer, we saw that they were about twelve times the size of our ship. They slowed down the engine and made several course changes to avoid them, but we had them only about sixty meters distant. Now we can still see some peaks in the distance, and it is feared that we may meet more tonight. This would be dangerous. May Jesus do as he pleases."

Mother Cabrini's primary concern was the well-being of her "Daughters," especially when they were seasick and frightened. But she also made it her business to visit with the hundreds of poor immigrants on every ship. She talked and prayed with them, and brought them food and comfort. Just as easily, she mingled with wealthy European and American passengers on every trip too. She had in mind several goals: convert these men and women to Catholicism, or recall them to the religion if they had not been practicing.

She also described her mission work in vivid detail, then solicited donations. The wealthy passengers were her captive audience on the deck—Mother Cabrini seized the opportunity of the long voyages to tell them about the destitution she encountered among poor immigrants, explaining her plans to feed their souls and bodies, if only she had more funds. Many were so moved by these stories that they offered donations before she had a chance to ask, which she graciously accepted. She was even more pleased if one of them promised to return to the Catholic Church. In a letter Mother Cabrini sent from one ocean crossing, she wrote:

"A very jolly millionaire from New York came on board. He is not Catholic, nor has he any religion. He says that does not matter but he has a great respect for us. He seeks always to be near us and entertains us with his useful and delightful stories. I wish that he would be converted and do something for us. Help me pray for this intention."

As soon as Mother Cabrini arrived back in New York, she visited Archbishop Corrigan to find out the details about the Jesuit priests' offer of their property in Poughkeepsie, just up the river from the city. It was called Manresa, and everything about it intrigued Mother Cabrini. By now she had learned to pay attention to good fortune that seemed to appear out of nowhere. It could be a sign of God's gentle nudging in the direction along a path she should take.

She made arrangements to visit the property immediately. The small apartment for orphans on Fifty-Ninth Street and the makeshift school at Saint Joachim church were woefully inadequate for the number of families the Sisters wanted to help. This country location might be able to house many more children in a safer, healthier environment.

Sister Aurelia joined her on a train ride out of Manhattan heading north along the banks of the wide, brown, slow-moving Hudson River. At the station, they were greeted by two Jesuit priests who dutifully brought them to the property. She recognized the scene instantly. This was the very house that had appeared in her dream in Codogno. The men showed her all the rooms in the main house, then the barn and stables. Finally, they led her and Sister Aurelia through a small field to the edge of a bluff that overlooked the Hudson River.

Mother Cabrini took a deep breath as she looked out across the valley. Just as she had in her dream, she felt at home here—perhaps because the air was so clear that she knew her lungs, always prone to infection, might be healthy here. She turned to Sister Aurelia and said quietly, "This is where I wish to be buried, on this slope with a view of the river." The young Sister was taken aback and was about to protest the notion of Mother Cabrini dying, when the Jesuit priests beckoned them back to the house.

One of them named the price at which they were willing to sell the land. The figure was so low that Mother Cabrini thought at first that she had misunderstood—had she missed something?

The priests finally admitted the property's single drawback: The water source had run dry. There was no running water. But having been raised in the country by her father, a hard-working, experienced farmer, Mother Cabrini knew how to read certain signs of nature and so she agreed to purchase the property at the price they offered.

Then she walked around the perimeter of the property and across it several times, while quietly examining the positions of trees and shrubs, as well as the grasses and brambles beneath her feet. Most of the ground was brown grass, but in one small patch hidden by trees, the grass was bright green. Suddenly, she stopped. "Here," she said, indicating a spot on the ground beneath the brush. "Dig here. This is where there is water." Though skeptical, the priests nodded politely and agreed to order workers to dig at that spot. Then they took Mother Cabrini back to the train station to return to the city. Within a few days, word was sent to the Sisters in New York: Water had indeed been found beneath that very spot.

The Missionary Sisters of the Sacred Heart were always diligent, fast workers at whatever they tackled and in just a few months the spacious country home was transformed into a happy home for orphan girls. The children slept in the upper floors of the main house and their classrooms were on the bottom floor. In addition to their daily lessons, the girls were taught practical skills such as embroidery, sewing, and cooking.

West Park also served as Mother Cabrini's first American novitiate—a house where young women who wanted to join the Missionary Sisters of the Sacred Heart could receive their training. The country air was so clear and revitalizing that for years to come *La Madre* insisted that the Sisters' periodic retreats take place there. At the same time, she found a location in New York City to serve as a reception point for families and children on Fourteenth Street, not far from the Italian neighborhoods. This, she knew, would please Archbishop Corrigan. She realized the gruff man had been right—the Fifty-Ninth Street townhouse had never been an appropriate location for the children.

It was an exciting day when Archbishop Corrigan came to visit West Park. He was eager to see the property and what Mother Cabrini had done with it. She guided him around the land, proudly showing off the house and introducing him to the children. At the edge of the hill, he stopped to admire the vista. "This is truly a great accomplishment," he said. "I will do all I can to help you support this place. Far away from the city, these children now have a chance for a good life under the supervision of your Sisters. I should never have doubted your perseverance."

Mother Cabrini laughed. She had grown fond of Corrigan and was used to his stern nature. Now he was a true friend and advocate. "I thank you for being my wise counselor," she said.

"One word of advice," said Corrigan. "Make sure that you bring here every single man and woman who has given you a donation. They must see how well you've put their money to good use."

Later that evening, Mother Cabrini remembered these words and wrote notes to the Cesnolas and other wealthy couples who had been so generous to her, and invited them to visit. The very next weekend, Count and Countess di Cesnola came with her friends to enjoy a country outing, and to see her new West Park residence. The Countess gaily greeted Mother Cabrini upon arriving with her husband and several other couples. "My God, this is beautiful!" she cried out. "*Madre Cabrini*, you have found the most precious place on earth for the children!" She rejoiced at the idyllic scene, and proclaimed it God-given.

As the visitors walked around the property, they seemed almost intoxicated by a cool breeze coming from the river filled with the fragrance of blooming flowers. Mother Cabrini gazed at the happy scene. It seemed as if her missionary work had reached a pinnacle. But she knew in her heart that this was just the beginning. The number of children who needed such a place was much bigger than those who were lucky enough to be living there. And to accomplish more, Mother Cabrini also knew that she needed more Sisters—and not only those who were training in Italy, but American women who could join them here. As her Sisters had come to know quite well, even when *La Madre*'s face reflected a calm contentment, inside she was most likely calculating another seemingly impossible undertaking.

Chapter Eleven

LYNCHINGS IN NEW ORLEANS

Soon after her stay at West Park, Mother Cabrini set off on another trans-Atlantic voyage—this time back to Italy. It was late summer 1890, and this time her intention was to recruit Sisters who could work as teachers in the schools she was hoping to open in New York—and now possibly Nicaragua too. She also needed more money. With all this on her mind, Mother Cabrini found the sea voyage a welcome time of quiet. She wrote:

"Yesterday I felt the previous night's loss of sleep so much that I was unable to do anything. Today, however, I feel better and am able to spend a little time with you. My traveling companions are sensible and very much agree with me in not giving in to seasickness. Anna is always calm and tranquil; Elizabetta feels cold and does her best to cover herself. The weather is really cold, always like an April morning, but the air feels so pure and exhilarating that it is a pleasure to breathe. It is healthful, inspiring sublime thoughts, as if a heavenly aura surrounded us…The sea continues to be marvelously calm and still. Heaven seems to be mirrored in it, as well as the features of a soul surrounded by grace-given peace and intimate, unending joy."

When a Protestant woman with a little dog on the ship was attracted to the Sisters, Mother Cabrini forced herself to pet the animal in order to engage the Protestant woman in conversation. Although the woman seemed fairly attached to her own religion, Mother Cabrini gave her a cross. "Perhaps I'll be a Catholic!" the woman had blurted out, and Mother Cabrini beseeched her Sisters to pray that this would come true. Not only would the woman find a home in the Church, but she was a person of some influence and Mother Cabrini recognized that she may very well bring others with her.

Seeking funding for her many projects was a constant concern. For this reason, at the top of Mother Cabrini's Rome to-do list was to call on three pious women: Princess Francesca Massimo, Carlotta Antici Mattei, and Contessa Guendalina della Somaglia. The three friends had raised money for Mother Cabrini's residence house and school in Rome.

Now *La Madre* had a new request. She was quite at ease in the company of these extremely wealthy women. They came from old Roman families, and it amused her that they found her simple life so fascinating—they asked many questions about New York, what she had seen and done. Were they envious of her adventures? Her independence?

They listened intently as the nun, whose dark habit contrasted sharply with their colorful silk dresses, described the impoverished children, women, and men that she and her Sisters encountered every day in New York. They sat in the dimly lit apartment of Princess Massimo—a tall, quiet woman with an air of loneliness about her. Mother Cabrini did not need to exaggerate the bleakness, particularly when she described toddlers sleeping in corners of doorways at night, or apartments crammed with ten or twenty people, many who were ill.

The young women became emotional. Princess Massimo dabbed her eyes with her handkerchief. "How can we allow children to live this way? With no one to love them!" she burst into tears.

"It is a privilege that you must not ignore," said Mother Cabrini.

The mournful women now looked at her questioningly.

"A privilege? What do you mean?" said Contessa Guendalina della Somaglia.

Mother Cabrini said, "You have the privilege to do such good in the world—it can only be accomplished through kind-hearted people like you. All that we wish for these children can happen." The women hastily agreed to help her by donating the funds she would need.

Mother Cabrini was expecting the visitor, but when she opened her apartment door she was struck by the solemn beauty of the woman dressed in the black clothing of a nun. "Good afternoon, *Madre Cabrini*," said the visitor. "Thank you for allowing me to visit. I promise I will not take too much of your time." It was a cool, overcast day, and the visitor pulled her dark shawl close around her.

Well-educated and refined, Doña Elena Arellano had taken vows of chastity and poverty after her father, the Prime Minister of Nicaragua, had died. She had founded *la Casa de Huerfanas de Artes y Oficios*—the Orphanage of Arts and Crafts—to teach widows, prostitutes, and other women handicrafts by which they could earn an income.

Mother Cabrini smiled, studying the face of Doña Elena. She was in her mid fifties with dark brown intelligent eyes, and brown hair pulled back from her face. She spoke gently and had the poise of a diplomat.

"I met with Pope Leo last week, and he told me that you were here in Rome—and I felt that I had to come to see you. As you might know, I come from Nicaragua and I have taken over a school for girls in Granada that very much needs the help of you and your Missionary Sisters."

Mother Cabrini's interest was piqued. Never had she considered Central America as a place for her Missionary Sisters.

"I know, *Madre*, that your Institute has distinguished itself by helping the poor Italian immigrant families in New York City," said Doña Elena. "But I tell you that wealthy families in high standing—and their children—where I live are desperately in need of basic education, as well as spiritual guidance. Many Catholic people have lost their morals, their humility toward God!"

She waited a moment, then continued. "Our school can bring the entire community together in support of the children receiving a Catholic upbringing," said Doña Elena. "If you would consider coming to Granada, I would arrange for a school to be put under your direction."

The two were silent for a few moments. Mother Cabrini was thinking that she had barely established her small school and convent in New York. West Park was just getting organized. These places still needed much guidance.

"These girls come from families who can pay tuition, and I would make sure all your travel and living expenses would be provided," said Doña Elena.

Cabrini thought of China, her childhood dream of traveling to exotic locations to spread the teachings of Jesus and education, particularly for girls. She knew she would help, though she did not know exactly how or when.

"I will consider this idea," said Mother Cabrini. "And will let you know what I can do."

"Thank you," replied Doña Elena Arellano. She smiled and bowed her head slightly. Then she rose and left.

Letters from the Sisters arrived from New York with news of a crisis.

Illness and malnourishment were common among tenement renters whose children came to the Sisters' doorstep at Saint Joachim Church every day with deep, hacking coughs. Few people who became ill or injured in the slums ever saw a doctor. Diseases spread quickly in families. Women who suffered complications during childbirth sometimes died soon after, leaving children without a mother. Newborn babies died because no midwife or doctor had been able to attend the birth. Poor immigrants were often malnourished, which made them weak and vulnerable to illness.

News of the situation reached Italy—and Bishop Scalabrini insisted that a hospital had to be established in New York to serve poor Italian immigrants. It made great sense to provide a hospital specifically for Italians—they not only needed care, but a place they could trust with doctors who would understand them.

He instructed Father Morelli, the pastor of Saint Joachim, to open a hospital. He quickly found a building on 109th Street in New York, though there was little money for medical supplies.

Father Morelli was really a simple parish priest, not a hospital administrator, so it was not surprising that he was quickly overwhelmed by the new challenges. He sent a letter to Mother Cabrini, begging her for help, and to send her Sisters to work with him. From Italy, she sent a letter back, and agreed—reluctantly. The Scalabrinian priests in New York had already proven to be terrible administrators. They still had not paid the Sisters who taught in their Saint Joachim School. Furthermore, Mother Cabrini suspected that they were not as devoted to the pope as they should be.

But once she agreed, a group of Missionary Sisters traveled uptown every day to work in the small hospital, giving it their full attention and energy. Hearing of this new endeavor, Countess Cesnola and her daughters, Gabriella and Luisa, came to work side by side with the Sisters in the hospital too—but the efforts proved fruitless.

"We found everything in a miserable state," wrote one Sister to Mother Cabrini, "especially the lack of what is necessary for care of the sick." The Sisters went to beg for food and for money to buy supplies. Reading these reports in Italy, Mother Cabrini reacted with frustration.

Italians need a good hospital, and leaders who they could count on to provide the very best care, she thought. *Even without training, the Sisters were doing a far better job of running a hospital than these men!*

Mother Cabrini went to pray at the altar in Codogno. She remembered the disastrous last months when she was at the House of Providence, and Bishop Gelmini had suggested that it was time for her to found her own convent.

She now knew the answer: Perhaps it was time for her and her Sisters to start a hospital of their own. When she returned to her room, Mother Cabrini wrote a letter to Count Luigi Palma di Cesnola. He was a member of the small hospital board and would tell her honestly if her idea was valid.

She received his reply in two weeks. "By all means, yes, you must start a hospital," he wrote. "The need is great and I have seen the miracles you and your Sisters can accomplish with your immense dedication and love. I will help you any way I can."

Fear and suspicion of immigrants in America was growing. In March 1891, newspapers around the world reported a horrific incident. Mother Cabrini was in Rome when the headlines caught her attention. David C. Hennessy, the superintendent of police and the son of Irish immigrants, had been murdered in New Orleans five months earlier—a city rife with social and familial factions, particularly among Sicilians.

Thirteen Sicilian men from one of these factions were accused of Hennessy's murder, but were acquitted later by the jury. Inflamed with rage, a mob of vigilante citizens broke down the door to the prison, shot nine of the men dead, and dragged two more out onto the street and lynched them. Americans were sickened by the incident, but Italians in the United States were filled with dread, knowing full well what it implied: American law could not stop people who wanted to terrorize Italians at any time.

Italy asked for redress for the families of the victims killed, but the American government shrugged off the request. In turn, Italy's minister in America left for home. Now Americans turned against Italy, and spread rumors about the criminal nature of Italians and their plots to overthrow the American government.

Newspapers reported that in Wheeling, West Virginia, miners went on strike when their boss refused to fire two Italian workers, men they claimed were "allied to a nation that was trying to bring about a war with the United States." Fear and hatred for immigrants—who were accused of being anarchists, socialists, or just generally lawless—were rampant. Many Americans called for tighter immigration restrictions.

In Italy, Mother Cabrini read about these incidents in the newspaper, and was filled with fear and sorrow for the plight of Italian immigrants in New York and other cities. She thought of the children, who were usually overlooked in such tragedies. *Who was caring for them?*

Mother Cabrini returned to New York in the fall—this time with twenty-nine Sisters from Italy. They were enthusiastically greeted by the other Sisters, as well as other city officials. They immediately traveled north to the West Park residence to rest for a few days before fourteen of them were to leave on another voyage—this time to Nicaragua. On October 10, they boarded the ship called *New York* of the Pacific Mail Lines. After their tearful goodbyes in the New York harbor and much waving of handkerchiefs to their friends on shore, the Sisters began to explore the massive ship and found it pleasantly comfortable.

Within a few hours, though, a violent hurricane arose and the ship heaved deeply first to one side, then the other. In these terrifying times, Mother Cabrini and her Sisters prayed without stop. "The ocean was swollen as I had never seen it," wrote Mother Cabrini in a letter. "Mountains formed as if by magic, and deep valleys were seen. It seemed as if the ship were headed for ruin on those momentary precipices. On deck, the wind raged and threatened to shatter the cabins...Not one of the sisters was frightened in the midst of such a terrible storm, and all lay calmly in bed disposed to die peacefully, but always under the bedcovers. Instead, I spent the night in the salon, from where I could speak to the sisters as they rested, and we were able to encourage each another…

"Meanwhile, all prayed to Our Lady of the Rosary, in whose month we were traveling. We lit the Loreto candle, which is very effective against storms at sea. Our Holy Mother, who does not let anyone pray in vain, truly came to our aid, delivering us from extreme peril."

It was a clear, moonlit night. Mother Cabrini was sitting on the ship deck, gazing at the stars. The water was as calm as a lake. The storm had passed the day before—now it was as if it never happened. She felt relaxed, awake, and close to Jesus.

After sleeping for many hours, she was now eager to watch the magical moments of sunrise. Other passengers began to join her on deck, and stood at the rail as the shoreline of Cuba, and then Haiti, passed by in the distance. The Sisters awoke one by one and came on deck too. They gathered together and sang hymns that intrigued and comforted the other passengers.

At last the ship reached Colón, the port of Panama, where all passengers disembarked. Those traveling on boarded a train to take them across the isthmus to Panama City. Enchanted at the sight of palm trees and banana trees, brilliant red and purple hibiscus and bougainvillea, the Sisters pointed out the parakeets, parrots, and macaws perched in the trees and the monkeys that climbed the trunks. But they gasped at the sight of Indians walking along the road—barely clothed.

These are truly mission lands, thought Mother Cabrini. *The further inland I travel, the happier I am that I have come.* The sight of what they considered spiritual poverty moved her and the Sisters. The next ship was delayed, so the Sisters decided to hire a crew member to take them in a large rowboat to visit the city.

Sitting close the water in this boat was very different than looking down on it from a ship's deck. Mother Cabrini felt her old fear of water suddenly rise up, her throat constricting. She gripped the sides of the rowboat and tried to focus on a spot in the distance. But the joy of the young Sisters distracted her and helped keep her fear in check. The women now raised their voices and sang melodiously in the brilliant sunshine when suddenly a swarm of sea birds appeared out of nowhere and began to follow their boat.

"*Madre*, do you think these birds are a sign sent to us from God?" shouted one of the Sisters gaily.

"Why, yes, perhaps it is! I think that they must represent all the Sisters who will join us in the coming years," responded Mother Cabrini.

"Maybe they represent all the many souls that we must save in our lifetime!" said another Sister, laughing.

Just as Mother Cabrini was about to respond, an even larger flock of sea birds began to follow their boat as it cut through the waves. "Surely these are the souls who will be led to salvation by the Missionary Sisters of the Sacred Heart!" another Sister said. And this, they all agreed, was most certainly true.

It was early November when the women arrived in Granada at the shore of the freshwater Lake Nicaragua. An enthusiastic crowd of citizens and local officials surged around them in the bright mid-morning sun. *They want to make us martyrs at our first entry to venerate us in their excessive devotion,* thought Mother Cabrini.

Doña Elena Arellano had arranged for comfortable sleeping quarters for the Sisters. The school, with an attached chapel, was spacious and already well equipped. Although many families wanted to send their girls to the school, Doña Elena told Mother Cabrini that there would be room for only fifty students. The school had formed a parent council, which decided the school's tuition, she explained. Mother Cabrini took note of the high fee and said she hoped Doña Elena would allow her to enroll some poor students too.

Although their first days in Granada seemed to go well for the Sisters, the novelty of living in the tropics soon began to wear off. It was hard to sleep in the relentless heat. Scorpions and even snakes crossed their paths, indoors and out. The rumble of a nearby volcano could be heard intermittently and mild earthquake tremors unnerved the Sisters. Three fell ill with typhoid fever and were nursed by Mother Cabrini around the clock until, at last, they recovered fully.

A challenge of a different kind confronted Mother Cabrini: Certain men from elite families approached her hoping to enroll their children…children they had had out of wedlock. The illegitimacy of these girls became apparent when Mother Cabrini asked the fathers to see the children's birth certificates. Once she realized what was going on, she refused to enroll them in her school.

The fathers were angry. A few tried to bribe her, and when that failed, they made threats, hinting that it could be dangerous for her to stay in the country. But Mother Cabrini held firm. If she allowed them into her school, she reasoned, she would appear to be condoning immoral behavior.

Without incident, the school opened with fifty students and seventeen Missionary Sisters of the Sacred Heart working as teachers. They began by instructing the girls in the basics of literature and science, and added cooking, sewing, and other practical skills. Local women came to visit and help—and to meet Mother Cabrini. As a courtesy, they invited her to view the nearby volcano.

"I accepted this invitation for later, in order to be able, on my return, to give you some news about this country," wrote Mother Cabrini to her Sisters, "and also not to be like those who go to Rome without seeing the pope."

In six months, the school was running smoothly. The students were thriving and Doña Elena was thrilled, deeply grateful to see her dream come true. But in her typical fashion, Mother Cabrini was already planning her next trip. She had received a plea for help and had to leave for New Orleans as soon as she could.

Archbishop Francis Janssens of New Orleans, a gracious and usually reserved man, now sent an urgent letter pleading with Mother Cabrini to assist with the Italian immigrants in that city who were still traumatized and demoralized by the lynching that had taken place there. Mother Cabrini had already sent three Sisters from New York to New Orleans with instructions to locate possible buildings to purchase in order to open a school and an orphanage there.

Mindful of the proper protocol, she wrote: "Upon arrival, go to Father Gambera. Then visit the Archbishop and begin everything with his blessing."

By now, Mother Cabrini was shrewd in the business of buying property: "Make the acquaintance of a lawyer who knows

Italian well," she wrote to the Sisters going to New Orleans ahead of her, "one who is good and trustworthy, to help you in drawing up a contract with assurance and on generous terms."

She left Granada in April of 1892, and along with Sister Mercedes Cepeda, crossed Lake Nicaragua, passing majestic mountain peaks and green tropical forests. While waiting for the next steamship to arrive, she and Sister Mercedes took time to visit the Mosquito Reservation, where they respectfully approached the natives to speak with them.

"Here there was no Catholic church and no priest to visit the Indians of the Reserve, except for a visiting one who came four times a year," she wrote to her Sisters. "The government considers the Indians as a species of animal, and the Church has not been able to do anything about it. We visited the Indian district, and with a smile and a word here and there, we managed to win over these people, who responded by approaching us after they had overcome their shyness and the fearful awe they felt for the 'Black Robe,' as they call the religious, be they priests or nuns.

"We spoke to them of our holy faith, and what we had to say made them very happy. They asked me to send them priests and Sisters to save them."

Speaking to these men was especially meaningful—Mother Cabrini believed in the dignity of all human beings and was honored that they were willing to converse with her. She also wanted to show them that as a woman of faith, she recognized their goodness and wished them and their families well.

As a lover of nature, Mother Cabrini was captivated by the wild tropical landscape and the curious town of Bluefields, populated by African slaves who had escaped from ships, indigenous natives, and British colonialists. "You should see how pretty this town is!" she wrote to her Sisters. "All the houses have two stories, built in the style of the United States. It is truly beautiful, overlooking a charming bay, which gives it a continuous, cool breeze. The only disadvantage is that it lacks a Catholic church and Catholic schools, while there are five Protestant ministers who do everything."

She continued her journey to New Orleans, which was long and arduous. At one point Mother Cabrini became so sick with fever that she felt sure she was dying. "Trustingly, I asked Jesus at least to let me finish the journey," she wrote. "In His goodness, He heard me and finally today I feel well and have all my energy back."

Soon after arriving in New Orleans, Mother Cabrini began her search for an appropriate building in which to house her Sisters. She signed the papers to purchase a tenement building located on Saint Philip Street in the French Quarter, the heart of the poorest Italian immigrant community. The Sisters swept, scrubbed, and painted the two-story building, readying it to serve as a convent and parish church for Italians. It was hard work—the air was hot and thick with humidity and mosquitoes. Though the Sisters were thirsty, the cleanliness of the water was questionable and so they only sipped it warily.

But not long after they opened their doors, the Sisters found that their little church was filled to capacity on Sundays. To accommodate the eager churchgoers, they set up canopies over the courtyard to provide extra space, as well as shade. It was obvious that immigrants received the same rough treatment in New Orleans as they did in New York—and suffered the same dire conditions. They needed all the help that the Sisters could provide. As the nuns got to know the city, they began the daily routine of visiting families and ministering to those who were sick and housebound.

Prison visits were also part of their missionary work. The Sisters found Italian inmates, and stayed for hours to speak with them, pray with them, and listen to their stories. Prisoners became so calm after visits from the nuns that the director of the New Orleans prison gave permission to the Sisters to visit whenever they wished and to stay as long as they liked.

Among the crimes committed by the men in prison, murder was surprisingly rare. The nuns soon found out why: Murder was common, yet the perpetrators were dealt with by their own social, business, and family factions. New Orleans was one of the primary ports for the Sicilian fruit trade and Italians had lived there for decades. Serious crimes such as murder were rarely brought to the attention of the police.

And like New York, the city seemed to have more orphans than it could care for—the Sisters began to bring them into their convent and started a small school where the children could sleep, be fed, and were taught by loving teachers.

Realizing that the New Orleans foundation would soon need to expand, Mother Cabrini invited Mother Josephine Lombardi to come from the New York convent; she had established several foundations and was a highly experienced and competent administrator.

But funds were limited as usual, so the Sisters were forced to beg for money on the streets. Mother Cabrini, who advocated "humility, simplicity, and obedience," joined them. She never missed a chance to tap new sources of money, whether the amount was small or large. Years later, she called upon Captain Salvatore Pizzati, a New Orleans resident who had made a fortune in the shipping business. Mother Cabrini invited him to Saint Philip's, and when he saw the Italian orphans there, he spontaneously promised to make a large donation of $75,000 to build a new space for them. But some politicians and officials resented the fact that this money would be going to religious establishments; they believed that Pizzati's money should be spent on non-religious institutions.

Mother Cabrini realized that although she had the Captain's donation in hand, these men might find a way to revoke the gift. She immediately purchased a large piece of property on Esplanade Avenue. Before she signed the agreement, she went over and over it to make sure that each clause was concise and airtight. As she expected, certain local officials were furious. One approached her on the street and told her that the Italians of New Orleans opposed the orphanage. "Try, if you dare," she said, "to destroy this work, and you will pay dearly for it." The house was, indeed, built.

Chapter Twelve

SAFE HAVENS FOR ITALIANS

They had a few beds, sheets, and homemade mattresses, as well as some medicines—but not much else. And yet with these meager supplies and a lot of hard work, a major urban hospital would grow. In September 1892, Mother Cabrini and a small group of Sisters helped ten patients leave the hospital. It was shutting down due to unpaid debts incurred by the Scalabrinian Brothers.

The move was not easy. It was a cold and rainy morning and most of the patients could walk only haltingly. One young woman was too weak to stand at all without help. Medicines were packed up in suitcases and boxes. Sheets had to be folded and wrapped in twine so they could be easily carried. The Sisters bustled about, trying to keep the patients comfortable while moving them along to the horse and buggy waiting outside. The Sisters had found a better, more suitable building for the hospital on Twelfth Street in Lower Manhattan. After many hours, everyone and everything was finally moved.

Some church leaders, uneasy with a woman in any leadership role, accused Mother Cabrini of trying to amass power for the Missionary Sisters of the Sacred Heart. She was also criticized for supporting a hospital that served poor Italians instead of all Italians. Caught in the middle of these disputes, Archbishop Corrigan had been uncertain about supporting Mother Cabrini's plans for her own hospital. Finally, she went to see him to tell him plainly what she intended.

"I wanted to take over the old hospital in order to save it," Mother Cabrini said to Archbishop Corrigan, sitting across from him at the very desk where she first met him years ago. "But I will not pay its outstanding debts, which I did not incur!"

"But you do not have funds to start a hospital—and though I do not wish to be disrespectful, you do not have the expertise either," the Archbishop said to her.

"New York needs a solvent, well-run hospital for poor Italians who would otherwise be dying on the streets—this should be obvious," countered Mother Cabrini. "I know how to find the money for it—and I am sure doctors can be found in this city. I have already started many foundations with less than we have today."

The two were silent for a few moments. "I will tell you one thing for certain," she went on. "I am adamant that I will never again work with the Scalabrinian priests. I admire Bishop Scalabrini greatly, but these men have proven to be disorganized and utterly lacking in any business sense. They have been a disservice to their patients, to the Sisters, and to all Italians!" And finally, she told the Bishop, who by now was speechless, that she would find a suitable new location for the hospital—for a good price.

Once again Corrigan was stunned by the strength and determination of this petite woman. Her vision for the world was big—bigger than his own, if he were honest—and her dedication equally so. He relented and told her that she had his blessing. He also gave her the names of four wealthy Italians in New York who might make a donation to her hospital.

Obstacles would always present themselves in nearly any endeavor. But with patience and persistence, Mother Cabrini had seen many great goals achieved in the name of Jesus. She responded to people and situations that got in her way not with anger but with a firmer resolve to find solutions.

La Madre was forty-two years old, a mature, independent-thinking woman who loved and obeyed the words of Jesus and the pope in Rome. Her faith had grown stronger over the years. "Do not criticize, do not complain," she advised her Sisters in one letter. "If sometimes you get the itch to wag your tongue, wag it against yourself. Better still, practice the lesson taught by our lovable saint, Francis de Sales: keeping silent about others, speak neither good nor ill about yourselves."

This quality of not complaining, combined with her kindness and charm, inspired nearly everyone who met Mother Cabrini. Women chose not to marry and instead were moved to join the Missionary Sisters of the Sacred Heart. Officials offered to speed up bureaucratic procedures so that she could establish orphanages and schools as quickly as possible. And wealthy people found themselves making donations to her cause in far larger amounts than they gave to any other. She was a humble person who had the uncanny ability to draw out the best in others.

Yet she confided in her diary writings about her moments of feeling discouraged, unequal to the tasks before her. Often ill and weak, she had many dark hours when she wondered if she was dying. She could only accept her condition and wait until her strength returned. But even these times were useful because they made her empathetic to the weakest people wherever she went. Above all, she wanted to lift poor people out of the misery that came from lack of education, ill health, and the lack of a spiritual foundation—this was her ultimate motivation.

Now, with a horse and buggy and one donated ambulance, she and the Sisters had finally transported their small group of patients from the old hospital through the rain to the rented space that was to be their new hospital. It would be named in honor of Christopher Columbus, as it was the four hundredth anniversary of his arrival to America.

Mother Cabrini was right—help came from unexpected sources. A wealthy patron who wished to remain anonymous gave regular donations. A doctor named Eugenio Villari donated medical instruments. A nearby restaurant offered to provide water and food on a short-term basis. With some financial help from her friends the Cesnolas, Mother Cabrini and the Missionary Sisters of the Sacred Heart were able to purchase other supplies.

"It will mean that for the present we will have something small, and this will become large only when God pleases," wrote Mother Cabrini.

News about this new hospital for the poor quickly spread. Distinguished American and Italian-born doctors from around New York City offered to work there. A Medical Board was soon formed, consisting of doctors who would guide the hospital as it grew. Doctors on this Board took no fee—this was, after all, a charity hospital.

Among them was Dr. Gustavo Boucher, who was born in Naples and had worked as a professor in the Naval College of

Italy before coming to New York in 1890. His ability to converse in Italian and English made him an invaluable asset to the hospital. Mother Cabrini was the director, but because she traveled frequently, Mother Cherubina Nositti was appointed Superintendent. The Sisters worked as bookkeepers and clerks. They assisted the doctors in the pharmacy, laundered the bed sheets, and cooked meals for the patients. Although they were not trained as nurses, they ministered to the sick and offered as much care and comfort as they could. With the efforts of dedicated doctors and hard-working Sisters, Columbus Hospital became known for providing high-quality care for its mostly Italian patients.

Smallpox, scarlet fever, and measles—so many sick children arrived with these illnesses that an outpatient department for childhood diseases was added. More and more patients—a mix of Italians and poor people of other nationalities—found their way to Columbus Hospital every day, and the building became too small to accommodate them all. A new location was found on Twentieth Street, and under the guidance of the Medical Board, renovations were made to this larger space so that it suited the needs of the hospital. In 1895, Columbus Hospital became incorporated and on February 18, 1896, the hospital was dedicated by none other than Archbishop Corrigan.

This recognition was a big step for immigrants, and for the city. The hospital was an oasis for thousands of poor Italians who suffered ill health and had nowhere to turn. Here, they could trust doctors and nurses who spoke their own language. Here, they were served pasta and other food from their native Italy, and were even allowed sips of wine with meals. Here, they were among their own kind, and comforted by the Sisters, who reminded them of home.

Mother Cabrini visited with patients whenever she could. She prayed with them, and listened to stories of their families back home, as well as their fears and hopes for life in America. She was as loving to them as if she were, in fact, their mother. She wanted the best care for each individual. Her days were filled with actively seeking out donations and gifts from wealthy Italians in New York to sustain the hospital. With these, as well as money from patients who were able to pay, Columbus Hospital could provide free beds for poor immigrant patients.

Then came an unexpected boost: An Italian warship docked in New York with two sailors who had contracted typhoid. All the hospitals in the city refused to treat the sailors—except Columbus Hospital. In gratitude, the Consul General Giovanni Branchi declared that Mother Cabrini's hospital would receive a flat fee for treating any Italian sailor from a merchant vessel who needed medical attention in New York. Thus, Columbus Hospital continued to expand—treating one thousand patients in 1896 and approximately five thousand in 1903. Later, the hospital added a training school for nurses.

As upsetting as it was to see families living in abject poverty, Mother Cabrini found it almost as bad to discover how easily Italian immigrants were lured into Presbyterian churches. She observed the simple but effective strategy: Their clergy offered gift baskets to these families, filled with food and little toys for their children. So even while she worked hard to establish New York's Columbus Hospital, she said yes to an invitation from Bishop Charles McDonnell to open a school for boys and girls from Italian families in the Red Hook section of Brooklyn. The

Protestants had a stronghold there, and she did not want it to get stronger.

Gathering Sisters who were experienced teachers, she met with McDonnell—who had been secretary to Archbishop Corrigan—and together they worked to found the school he wanted; she named it Saint Charles School. The school was to be used as a kind of community center—a gathering place for Feast Day celebrations and family events, and where the Sisters could give religious instruction to anyone in the community who wanted it. Mother Cabrini wanted whole families to feel welcome at the church any day of the week. This sensitivity to the emotional and spiritual needs of all her people was a significant reason why *La Madre* was so beloved, and why her work endured.

And *all her people* meant those who were outcast or considered lost by others too. The Sisters in New York spent much time visiting Italian-born prisoners, most of whom were being held for unpaid debts or petty crimes. The Sisters sang hymns at Mass held by local priests in the corridors of the Ludlow Street Jail in Lower Manhattan or at Blackwell Island, and sat with the inmates for hours afterward. They gave the men rosaries and scapulars to remind them of their faith.

Naturally, Mother Cabrini and her Sisters were against capital punishment, and many Sisters stayed with inmates on death row during their last days and hours before execution, helping them to reconcile with God. They eased the men's minds by assuring them that their families would be well cared for.

When she and Mother Ignatius Dossena—who visited many prisons in the New York area—learned that a twenty-nine-year-old man was awaiting execution in Sing Sing, a prison located thirty miles north of New York City, they began to visit him together twice a week. In one of their early visits, Mother Cabrini gently asked him about his family.

"I have a daughter, *Madre*; she is only four years old. I love her with my whole heart, and it's because of her that I regret what I've done."

"Where is she now?" Mother Ignatius gently asked.

"She is with my aunt, who is very old, and not well enough to care for a child," the man said, and began to cry. "What have I done? I have not only ruined my life, but my daughter's life too." As the man wept, Mother Cabrini and Mother Ignatius exchanged looks.

"I will make a promise to you," said Mother Cabrini. The man lifted his head to stare at her. "Tell me where I can find your daughter, and we will go and bring her to our orphanage. There she will be cared for by the Sisters. She will be safe, she will eat good food every day, and play with other children."

"Thank you, *Madre*," he said. She gazed back at him, saying with her eyes that she was telling the truth, and that she would do as she promised.

When she described the poignant visits to her friend in Italy, Mother Cabrini wrote, "He was greatly consoled and even more so when we brought his young daughter to visit for their last kiss."

The two nuns stayed with the man the day before he was sent to the electric chair, where he died holding a crucifix given to him by Mother Ignatius.

Prisoners knew of Mother Cabrini and deeply appreciated her kindness toward them. One Sing Sing inmate named Pasquale Cappelli expressed his gratitude to Mother Cabrini in a flowery letter on the occasion of the twenty-fifth anniversary of the founding of the Missionary Sisters of the Sacred Heart:

"Yes, it is in the name of all the Italians who have the misfortune of being enclosed in this house of pain that I send you this letter, in order to make myself the interpreter of the immense appreciation and gratitude which we all have in the deep recesses of our hearts for the kind, loving, charitable assistance, help and counsel with the Sisters of this never-sufficiently-praised institution of which you, Reverend Mother, are the worthy Foundress, daily bring to us…

"We would be most remiss if we permitted this great occurrence of the twenty-fifth anniversary of the foundation of this institute to go by unnoticed, and if we did not extend to you with true and deep feelings of appreciation our devoted thanks…"

Sing Sing had no chaplains who spoke Italian, so Mother Cabrini found one who worked with the Sisters in New York, Father Alexander Indelli, and convinced him to visit the Italian inmates as often as he could. Whenever they could, the Sisters advocated for prisoners, and in at least one instance, were able to convince the governor of New York to commute the death sentence of an Italian inmate to life in prison.

Just as she witnessed the tremendous success of all her projects, Mother Cabrini lost one of her dearest supporters: Monsignor Serrati. News of his death came at the end of a long day of going over the curriculum with Sisters who were teaching at the Saint Charles School. She took the letter into her room on Roosevelt Street, sensing that it contained bad news.

It was a brief note, sent by her Sisters at Codogno. Her heart ached—she had recently been thinking and even dreaming about Serrati. He had always been protective, encouraging, supportive, and loving toward her. He had seen her grow up!

Because of him, she had worked at the House of Providence, where she learned so much about working faithfully in difficult circumstances, and then founded the Missionary Sisters of the Sacred Heart.

He was a simple country priest, but he had given her the courage to travel to lands he himself could barely imagine. She lit a slender white candle on her table and, falling to her knees, she prayed for his soul and gave her thanks for all she had learned from this wise man whom she would never see again.

La Madre ached to go back to Italy, to see her beloved Pope Leo XIII, and to visit her foundations. It was time to bring back more Sisters who would be ready for true missionary work. It was September 1892, and two hundred Missionary Sisters of the Sacred Heart now lived and worked in fourteen houses located in Italy, America, and Central America. Mother Cabrini kept in touch with them as much as she could, and to do so she traveled constantly.

She made ongoing plans for the Sisters' development and training. She purchased buildings to be used for summer residences, and she organized regular retreats and classes. When she was traveling at sea, she wrote long encouraging letters to help the Sisters face all their challenges.

In one she wrote, "In their mute language, the elements teach us how to act toward those who are angry with us or want to harm us. Let us set our sights a bit higher, never fixing our gaze on the creature. Let us try to see, instead, the disposition of the Most High, never criticizing or complaining about the person who hurts us. Let us pity and excuse the person, as David did when he felt gravely abused. He did not allow any retaliation but said: 'Let him say what he wants, because it is God who allows this against me and it is less than I deserve.'

"This is how a soul conformed to the heart of God acts. May such fine, great virtue be ours! Let us ask for it with great urgency. May it enter in us, unite itself to our bones, our marrow! Then holiness will become easy."

Whenever she visited one of her foundations, she spent time speaking with each Sister personally so that she could evaluate her temperament and talents. Who had the gift for teaching? Who had the skills for cooking meals for large groups of Sisters and children? Who was good at organization and administration? Who had the necessary patience and kindness to care for small children? She strived to cultivate the best instincts in them all.

In joining the order, the women willingly embraced a life of poverty and hardship in dedication to serve to the poor. Obedience was a highly valued spiritual concept. Mother Cabrini instructed her Sisters: "Remember that no one becomes a saint without obedience. As a matter of fact, the favorite virtue of all the saints was obedience. Do not do things by halves, oh daughters, but let your obedience be complete and perfect than that of Jesus."

But kindness was at the heart of all of Mother Cabrini's disciplining of the Sisters. She never scolded anyone in front of others, and always made sure they knew how much she cared for them, no matter what they had done or not done.

One Sister remembered, "One morning I had been given a severe scolding by *La Madre*. Later that day, I went into the dining room and there on the table was a large ripe apple. I asked the Sisters where it had come from and they answered me that Mother Cabrini had placed it there. I knew she had done this for me, so I went to find her. She said, 'Are you still convinced that I spoke to you for your own good? Go in peace, and do the same with those for whom you are responsible, all the days of your life. Tell them the facts of their faults, and then give them encouragement.

"Do not ever leave a person without a kind word that will show that you love them and you desire only to help them."

Mother Cabrini called the Sisters "Daughters" because she really felt as if they were her children. She took note if anyone was sick or if a Sister needed an extra confidence boost. When one young Sister admitted how afraid she was of strangers, *La Madre* asked her to take up collections every Sunday so she could get to know people. Feeling an enormous sense of responsibility for the hundreds of Missionary Sisters, Mother Cabrini prayed to Jesus for guidance and help, and that her motivation always be for the good of these women who had been entrusted to her.

Now in Codogno, she prayed with particular intensity for the safety of the Sisters in Nicaragua. The country was in the midst of yet another revolution—and she knew many Nicaraguans viewed the Church as an enemy. "*Che Dio li protegga…*"

Her fear was well founded. At that very time, a young woman from a family of high social standing in Granada had shown up unexpectedly at the school and begged the Sisters to take her in. She was young, intelligent, and pretty—everyone knew that she attended every ball in Granada. But after one long night, she apparently had a sudden change of heart—and announced her wish to be a nun.

The Sisters hesitated and refused to admit her as quickly as she wished. After all, this desire could be another passing whim.

But the young woman appealed to Doña Elena Arellano, who gladly accepted her. Family and friends objected to the young woman's wish, and were angry at Doña Elena Arellano.

A rumor began to spread that the Sisters had convinced the girl to turn her back on her family and join the Missionary Sisters of the Sacred Heart. The situation came to a head late one morning, when the air was clear and cool after rain, and the birds were squawking cheerfully high in the tree branches. The Granada school was in session as usual, and all was calm.

Children were grouped in their classrooms, and through the open windows, their teachers could be seen standing before them, giving lessons and asking questions. In a small room near the administration office, one young Sister was sewing a new uniform and humming softly to herself. Loud voices erupted at the front entrance of the school and a man boomed out a command asking all the Sisters to come to the front door immediately.

The Sister who was sewing set aside her work and rushed to find out what was happening. She arrived at the front door at the same moment as the Mother Directress, who demanded to know who the men were. The city's prefect, Mr. Pedro Pablo Bodan, and the governor, Mr. Rivos, introduced themselves and explained they had been sent by their superiors to remove the Sisters from the school and send them out of the country immediately. Some Nicaraguans were adamantly against religious influence and were now prepared to make sure the Sisters left.

The Mother Directress angrily demanded to see papers that spelled out the terms of their departure, and told the men that it was impossible anyway because two Sisters were ill and in bed. The men responded that time was of the essence, and she saw in that instant they were right: The school was surrounded by soldiers holding rifles, which she presumed were loaded.

She ran to get the other Sisters out of their classrooms and living quarters, shouting at them to pack quickly what they could. The young students began to scream and cry at the sight of the distraught Sisters rushing around trying to gather their belongings. What was happening?

The soldiers remained in their places, guns in hand, as the Sisters began to say hasty goodbyes to the students and to a few parents who had arrived at the school upon hearing the news. The stern-faced soldiers surrounded the Sisters and marched them out of the school, forcing them to walk single file down a path to the lake, where a boat waited for them. Clouds covered the sun and the air was chilly—the Sisters pulled their coats around their shoulders.

As they walked, a crowd of local residents, parents, and friends gathered along the path, crying out to the Sisters, but were blocked by the soldiers. Doña Arellano ran along in the crowd too, begging the soldiers to allow her to go with the Sisters. They told her that if she went with the Sisters, she would never be allowed back into her country. She gladly joined them.

"Wait!" The young Sister who had been sewing peacefully just hours earlier stopped short in the line. The soldiers halted too, glaring at the young nun in disbelief. "I forgot my slippers!" she explained loudly. "I must go back—it will take just a few minutes!" Stunned by the nun's boldness, the soldiers did not have time to react as she turned and ran back up the hill and into the convent. With their fingers on the triggers of the guns, two soldiers ran after her. Within a few minutes she emerged, triumphantly holding the slippers over her head.

Angrily, the men now hurried the women to the waiting boat. As soon as all the nuns were accounted for, the vessel left the dock. As if God were crying, rain began to fall at that very moment. The frightened Sisters looked back at the receding shoreline, now veiled in a mist of rain, the white sand and clear waves lapping at the beach, and the deep green trees lining the coast. Still in shock at how fast they had been expelled, the women cried for the students and families they had come to know and love.

The boat headed along the coast of Panama. Once the Sisters understood where they were being taken, they talked about what to do when they arrived. It was agreed: They would immediately send Mother Cabrini a cablegram to tell her of their predicament.

At the time Mother Cabrini was in the middle of a whirlwind trip in Italy. She had met with Pope Leo XIII, who expressed his love for her and all that she and her growing number of Sisters were able to do. She confided in him her desire to travel to South America, and he was pleased.

But now she read the distressing news of the Sisters being expelled from their school in Nicaragua—one that they had worked so hard to establish. Although she worried for the well-being of the young women and Doña Arellano, Mother Cabrini was not an alarmist. She knew that their missionary work would continue, perhaps even in Panama. "If today they do not want us in one country anymore, we shall go to another," she said, "shaking the dust from our shoes just like the apostles."

Chapter Thirteen

CROSSING THE ANDES

The sun was setting on the clear, calm water. Alone, *La Madre* went out onto the deck of the steamer *Mapocho*, and found a chair facing east. Was that the lighthouse? She leaned forward, straining to see the landmark near the school in Panama, which she had just left.

In only a year, the Sisters who had been expelled from Nicaragua had founded a school in Panama, which was now flourishing. Eager to be among these Sisters again and to reassure them with her presence, Mother Cabrini visited them in their tropical location and stayed for more than three weeks. It was a welcome stop on her longest journey so far. She was on her way to Buenos Aires to fulfill a long-held desire to start a foundation there.

Now sadness swept over her as she thought about the Sisters and their students in Panama—she already missed their youthful exuberance and their eagerness to learn. She fixed her gaze on the tiny spot where she believed the school was located, and imagined the Sisters praying right at this moment for her safety. Her heart reached out across the water to them, and she felt their hearts reaching back to her.

Later that night, she wrote to them: "I continued looking intently to the left of the lighthouse, but little by little, even it became imperceptible and finally there was darkness all around me. Having abandoned all hope of seeing you again for now and of hearing your voices, which a little earlier had sung the 'Ave Maris Stella,' I, too, retired to rest."

Her traveling companion for this long sea voyage was Mother Chiara, who quickly became so frightened and seasick by even the smallest waves that she took to bed immediately. Mother Cabrini tried not to laugh at the young nun, who cried dramatically that she could not eat at all while on board the ship, and feared the trip would end in all of them drowning. "*Sii coraggioso!*" Mother Cabrini told her. By now, Mother Cabrini had crossed the seas many times, and had learned that steam ships were remarkably sturdy and were able survive the hard pounding of storm waves.

She eagerly awaited the moment when the ship would cross the equator. Would the weather be noticeably different? Would the sun be bigger, hotter? But when the moment came, she was surprised that the air was in fact cool, not at all as humid or warm as she expected. The passing landscapes fascinated her, as the ship moved along the waters of Ecuador, then Peru. It docked many times and the two women went ashore as much as they could—Mother Chiara was always relieved to be on *terra firma*. Mother Cabrini was eager to explore Catholic churches and visit priests and bishops who resided in the port cities along the South American coast—many of which reminded her of Italy.

In Lima, they visited the relics of Santa Rosa, the 16th-century recluse known for her severe acts of penance, and for feeding and caring for the poor, whom she invited into her home. Santa Rosa, it was said, would lie face down on a large wood crucifix in prayer and asked to be tied to it, so that she could imitate the suffering of Jesus. While viewing these relics, Mother Cabrini prayed to the saint, asking her to bless the trip to Buenos Aires and make it possible to build a school there.

Finally, the *Mapocho* reached the port of Valparaiso in Chile. "What a magnificent port!" wrote Mother Cabrini to her Sisters. "It resembles the one in Genoa, very favored by nature. The city seems charming, and sprawls enough to look larger than it is, because it is built on the slope of a hill, or better said, at the foot of the Cordilleras. It is rather steep so that traveling from the lower part of the city, which consists of a straight row of houses, one ascends to the upper part by a funicular railway resembling a residential elevator. Looking out its small windows, we can see that we are going up a steep precipice. M. Chiara closed her eyes to avoid getting dizzy."

Now Mother Cabrini and Mother Chiara had a choice: Continue by ship around the Strait of Magellan to reach Buenos Aires? Or travel over the Andes mountains by mule? Because Mother Chiara had been traumatized throughout most of the sea travel, Mother Cabrini allowed her to make the decision. Her answer was immediate: "A hundred times the Cordilleras de Andes but not one more day at sea!" Mother Chiara nearly shouted.

If there were ever a doubt that Mother Cabrini was an intrepid and brave traveler, this next short episode in her life put that doubt to rest. In spite of being short and physically weak, she willingly faced great risk. Once they decided to travel by land, the two women visited the capital of Chile, Santiago. They were eager to keep going, but were forced to wait in that city for twenty-five days because their guides advised that deep snow on the high pass made travel impossible.

But they were warmly welcomed by priests and nuns, government officials, and wealthy citizens—all of whom tried in vain to convince Mother Cabrini to change her plans and remain in Santiago and start a school. At last, carrying gift baskets of fruit, sweets, and wine given to them by local nuns, the two women were able to board the train with other passengers to go to the foot of the Andes.

The slow train chugged steadily upward, drawing them closer to the mountains that now loomed majestically against the starkly bright blue sky. After many hours, the train stopped at the little town of Los Andes, and the two women were invited to spend the night in a small local convent. "We had a good breakfast that, in the keen air, seemed to taste more delicious than usual," she wrote in a letter. "The pastor of the town blessed us and gave us his best wishes for our trip."

They continued by train, up and up, alongside a rushing river, through a narrow tunnel, and finally to the end of the track. Now the forty-five passengers got off the train and were guided to waiting stagecoaches. For five long hours, mules pulled the coaches along a narrow path next to the quick-moving water in gorges below. At last, they arrived at Juncal, another tiny village. A kindly old shepherd appeared and offered to take Mother Cabrini and Mother Chiara to an inn with good beds. Mother Cabrini secretly named him Saint Joseph. That night they ate a dinner of tough meat and hard black bread—but were grateful for the meal, as the high altitude and cold temperature had made them ravenously hungry. They slept well, but not for long.

At four a.m. they were awakened by one of the guides—they were going to cross the high Cumbre Pass, and needed to take advantage of the clear weather. The women got up and quickly dressed in the dark, putting on long cloaks made with brown fabric and fur given as a gift from a group of Chilean women in Santiago. "We looked like two Capuchin Friars," wrote Mother Cabrini, "but the cold was beginning to be felt in those gorges and the coats served us admirably."

Each of the passengers then mounted mules and the caravan of travelers and guides began a slow climb up a mountain path in the early hours of dawn, winding along steep drops. Suddenly, the path disappeared beneath heavy, white snowdrifts. The group had no choice but to go on. One by one, the mules and their riders trudged through the treacherous drifts, sometimes only guessing where the path might be. Mother Cabrini looked back at Mother Chiara.

"How are you faring?" she called out, knowing her traveling companion to be anxious. Mother Chiara, now frightened more than she had ever been at sea, was slumped over the neck of her mule, and refused to lift her head to look in any direction. "I will be all better when we reach flat land again!" she replied.

Just then, a shout from a guide made them all stop short. A large crevice had opened in the path—each person would have to jump over it to continue onto the other side. Because she was at the head of the line, Mother Cabrini would have to go first. She slipped off her mule and looked at the gap. The guide she named Saint Joseph offered to help but she declined—yet he stood on the opposite edge, watching her carefully, as she got ready to leap.

She pulled her cloak close around her body and jumped. What she hadn't calculated was how much the thin air had weakened her. In a flash, she realized she was not going to make it to the other side. In that same instant, her Saint Joseph threw himself on the ground and caught her in his arms, pulling her up and over to safety. Her heart was beating so fast that Mother Cabrini felt as though she was dying. She fell back onto a snowdrift and closed her eyes, ready to meet Jesus, telling the guide to go help the others. After a short time, she revived, although she was very cold. She stood up and dusted the snow from her clothing. Now that everyone had reached the other side of the crevice, the guides led the passengers and mules along the path. After many grueling hours, the group reached a high pass near the volcano Aconcagua, which soared above twenty-two thousand feet. Though the air was thin and cold—and Mother Chiara was still in a state of quiet panic—Mother Cabrini relished the wide, open view of peaks and sweeping landscapes.

"What an imposing sight!" she wrote to her Sisters later. "How majestic! It seemed as though you could see the whole world there at the boundary between Chile and Argentina." She wanted to linger, but the guides saw ominous clouds gathering and hurried the travelers onward. Snow began to fall, and soon a thick fog obscured the mountains. The descent in Argentina was steep, and as the air grew colder, Mother Cabrini's mule slipped here and there on the narrow path.

At last, they came to an inn where the hostess, anticipating their arrival, served them a hearty warm meal. The innkeeper, asking the passengers about their impressions of the journey, was surprised when Mother Cabrini responded, "It was one of the most beautiful and fondest of all my voyages." From there, the passengers climbed aboard stage coaches and proceeded down a narrow route along the Mendoza River, arriving in Punta de Vacas.

The next stop was the city of Mendoza, where Mother Cabrini and Mother Chiara were welcomed by the Sisters of the Good Shepherd. The two women agreed: It was a great relief to find themselves safely in a religious house after that perilous, nerve-wracking journey. The following night the women crossed the pampas—immense, wide plains. They looked forward to reaching their final destination of Buenos Aires—where no one would be there to greet them.

In a chance meeting years before in Genoa, Mother Cabrini had been introduced to a citizen from Buenos Aires named Father Broggi. Now she and Mother Chiara set about to find him in the vast city. Buenos Aires, with its beautiful parks and elegant European architecture, appealed to Mother Cabrini. Yet in some aspects it reminded her of New York: Within a few blocks of the affluent neighborhood called Recoleta lived some of the poorest people of the city, housed in low, primitive shacks.

After two hours of searching for Father Broggi, the women located his home and knocked on his door. "Hello, may I help you?" he asked when he opened the door and saw the two rather dusty, disheveled nuns on his doorstep.

"*Ciao, Padre Broggi, sono La Madre Cabrini*…and this is Mother Chiara. *Abbiamo viaggiato a lungo*…we have just arrived, having traveled, well, from New York. I believe you and I once met in Genoa…"

"*Sì, naturalmente!*" said Father Broggi, his face breaking into a wide smile. "Please come in—and let me take those bags." He stepped aside so they could enter his small townhouse, and then picked up their heavy bags and brought them into his foyer.

125

"Come in, come in—would you like some tea or water?" Upon being addressed in their native Italian, the two women immediately relaxed and smiled. He led them into his sitting room and then clapped his hands together. "Tell me how you came here—a long, long journey indeed! And what is your purpose in this visit?" As Mother Cabrini explained the route they had taken in the last several months, Father Broggi's eyes widened. And when Mother Chiara told of how they had just crossed the Andes, he jumped up with surprise. "This is quite amazing—I am very glad that you survived! Now, I must invite you to stay here tonight. I will prepare a fine Italian dinner—yes, I am sure you have missed such food. Then I will make arrangements for you to stay with the Sisters of Mercy of Savona. They have been here in Buenos Aires for more than twenty years and would be most honored to receive you." How could they resist? It was such a pleasure to be welcomed by this kind man.

The next day he insisted upon taking them to meet the archbishop, the Most Reverend Monsignor Ladislaus Castellano. The two men were impressed with *La Madre*'s vision for starting a school and offered to introduce her to influential people in the city. One of these was Father G. Nepomucene Kiernan, a holy man who was very ill but who promised to help Mother Cabrini fulfill her wish. The first business was to find the right location for a school.

La Madre was always very particular when it came to choosing such spots. She weighed the cost with the surrounding neighborhoods, the space needed, and the pleasing aspects of the buildings themselves. After looking at about sixty houses in Buenos Aires, she found one that was "lovely, spacious, and well lighted," she wrote to her Sisters. She was discouraged from buying it by some of her new friends who doubted that she could find enough pupils to fill it. But her instinct spoke loud-ly—and Mother Cabrini purchased the building, though it was at a higher price than she liked. Negotiations were not easy for her because the only language she spoke well was Italian. As she wrote to the Superior of the foundation:

"I have to struggle with the problem of the language, not having anyone to talk to me, and with the difficulties of keeping the house clean while Mother Chiara attends to the kitchen. On the other hand, it is amusing; it seems as though I have returned to the times of the beginning of the Institute, when first one thing then another was found wanting. It reminds me also of the foundation in Rome where I was with another frail sister, Mother Serafina, just like Mother Chiara.

"I have to do everything—serve the priest, ring the bells, and be the altar boy—at least until the Sisters arrive to relieve me a little. Here, matters are more serious because the sisters whom I have called will not arrive before another month's time. I must have patience. In this way, this foundation will have its own story; and later on, we shall joyfully talk about it together. On the first day that I swept the parlors, my hands were full of blisters; but now my skin is quite accustomed to hard work."

She had written to Sisters in New York and Codogno, asking those who were prepared as teachers to come to Buenos Aires as soon as possible to start the school. One month later they arrived, and when more and more families sought to enroll their children, Mother Cabrini had to ask more Sisters to come to Buenos Aires to keep up with the demand.

Mother Cabrini wisely created a committee of eight accomplished women prominent in Buenos Aires society, and invited Mrs. Leonora Tezanos Pinto, the wife of the president of Argentina, to be the school's "godmother." A grand celebration honoring the school's founding took place on May 8, 1897. The mayor of Buenos Aires sent gardeners to decorate the house with flowers and ferns. Men from the local Catholic Club brought in carpets and curtains. A small orchestra was hired. Archbishop Ladislaus Castellano celebrated Mass, many speeches were made, and young girls delighted the audience by singing songs and performing a show in which Santa Rosa and Jesus appeared in the middle of clouds and colored lights. Mother Cabrini named the school Santa Rosa, in honor of the blessings of the saint who had guided this mission to success.

Now that the foundation was firmly established, her incessant desire to keep moving overcame her, and soon she was making plans to return to Italy by way of Barcelona. There she hoped to establish a new foundation, for it was clear that she would need Spanish-speaking Sisters to teach in her many Central and South American schools.

Chapter Fourteen

A NEW CENTURY AND NEW ADVENTURES

The night was pitch black and the air was cold, but inside the convent at Milan, the mood was merry. The Missionary Sisters of the Sacred Heart stood around the sturdy wood table where they ate their meals together. Now they raised their glasses to toast the new year. They sipped at small glasses of aged wine—a gift from one of the villagers. It was late, but the women—most of them still in their early twenties—were wide awake, ready to celebrate the momentous occasion. "This is the last night of the century!" said one with a cheerful laugh. It was New Year's Eve, 1899.

They were prepared to greet the new year with hope, good will, and their youthful missionary spirit. Church bells suddenly began to sound around the city. It was the moment to toast.

"*Che questo anno sia ricco di gioia per tutti!*" said Mother Cabrini, and they all drank.

Easily the shortest in the group, Mother Cabrini beamed with joy in the company of these Sisters. A plate of fresh biscotti appeared and was passed around, which the nuns ate happily between expressions of "*Felice anno nuovo!*" Soon after, they each trailed off to their rooms for bed. Mother Cabrini retired to her comfortable but simple room—one she came back to as often as she could.

She lit a candle and knelt to pray. After many quiet minutes in which she opened her heart to the love and wisdom of God, she rose to go to bed. But instead of sleep, she was drawn to the window—she opened the shutters and gazed out into the night.

1900! What would this new year, new decade, new century bring? Only a few weeks before, she and the Sisters had celebrated the feast day of their patron saint—Saint Francis Xavier, founder of the Jesuits, patron of Catholic missions, who was born in 1506. Mother Cabrini identified with this saint who was a dedicated missionary. *If I can accomplish just a fraction of what he did*, she thought.

This year she would be fifty, a milestone. She was grateful for her health—she so often suffered from fevers, bronchitis, and chest colds—and especially to be among her Sisters on this night. She felt the strength of Jesus surround her. She reflected on the last few years, and saw that they had been…full of miracles. There was no other way to describe her adventures and achievements. She had established houses in the United States, with dedicated Sisters from Italy and America too. She had crossed the Andes—no small feat, even Mother Cabrini could acknowledge this. She shook her head in wonder, remembering that leap she took to cross the deep crevasse, and how the shepherd caught her arm at the last second!

She had established a foundation in Buenos Aires, and made so many new friends there—some were quite wealthy, and eager to help fund her projects. After that, she had gone to Barcelona and now smiled as she remembered the charming Genoese gentleman who had offered to show her that city. He had been so polite and refined that she had accepted. He had taken her and several other Sisters to breakfast—what a fine treat!—then hired a coach to drive them around to see the public gardens, churches, and other points of interest in the city. It had been an exquisite day!

One horrible month she wished she could forget. An Ursuline community had claimed that a sum of money had been promised to them by Bishop Gelmini—years ago!—which he had donated to the Missionary Sisters of the Sacred Heart instead. The Ursulines brought the matter to the Congregation of the Religious and then worked to discredit the reputation of the Missionary Sisters. Mother Cabrini had been forced to appear in court to defend herself. How dare they try to tarnish the reputation of the Bishop! She could not allow it. The outcome was good—in the end, the Cardinal Prefects decided in favor of the Missionary Sisters of the Sacred Heart. What an ordeal! But the cardinals had stepped forward to support her—and this was worth more than gold.

Her thoughts turned to her beloved Pope Leo—he was now eighty-nine years old. Whenever she saw him, her heart was filled by his kindness—he was so much like a father to her.

Another treasured memory was the ten-day spiritual retreat she went on with forty Sisters from Codogno. Long stretches of prayer and reflection that restored her body and soul—how she loved that time!

Laughing to herself, she recalled meeting Countess Spottiswood Mackin in Paris. With help from this wealthy American woman, Mother Cabrini had finally opened a foundation there, although only after plenty of opposition. She and the Sisters found the townhouse given to them too luxurious, so they slept in the servants' rooms. This countess had been surprisingly humble and had a witty sense of humor. Mother Cabrini liked her immediately.

Always on the lookout for wealthy citizens whenever she traveled, she was able to identify men and women who sympathized with her missions and could donate funds, often making lifelong friends of them. But Countess Spottiswood Mackin had materialized out of nowhere—a true gift. And now she had lost touch with her and wondered where she had gone.

After Paris came London. Mother Cabrini loved to explore new cities. London was a gem, with its fine museums and the charming courtesy of its citizens. When she had become lost on the subterranean trains, several good-hearted Londoners kindly guided her back in the right direction. Yes, there was a lot of goodness in the world. And goodness could grow and multiply.

So much had been done this year—thanks to her hardworking Sisters. They were doing the difficult daily work of caring for the sick, and teaching in schools and caring for children of all ages in orphanages, with almost nothing. They had left their families and home towns, and, called by the missionary spirit, now worked to help those in need all over the world.

Mother Cabrini recognized that she herself had grown and changed. As her vision for foundations around the world became real, she had, by necessity, become a skilled businesswoman—negotiating for good purchase prices on buildings, educating herself on the legalities and bank regulations necessary for buying property, and dealing with businessmen and male civic leaders who made it clear that they did not think much of her because she was woman—and an Italian woman at that. She had learned to confront them, outwit them, and wear them down with her persistence. These were skills that most women of the time were not given the chance to develop.

Finally, Mother Cabrini went to bed. As she closed her eyes, her thoughts turned to the future. She had so much work still to do—where would she go next?

The news was upsetting.

It was a brilliantly sunny but windy day aboard the ocean liner *Alfonso XIII* that had departed from Genoa and was heading to Buenos Aires. Mother Cabrini was strolling on the deck with her traveling companions, Sister Anna and Sister Michelina, when she was surprised to see a familiar face in the crowd of passengers strolling on the deck—Father Terradas!

She had met him in Buenos Aires six years earlier, and now he greeted her warmly and said he had recently returned from Panama. "Tell me, how are my dear Missionary Sisters there?" asked Mother Cabrini. A brisk wind blew across the ship's deck, making her habit flap around as if she were a bird ready to take flight.

"Not well at all, I am sorry to tell you," said Father Terradas. "Diseases that ravage that country...yellow fever, smallpox, typhoid...have afflicted the Sisters, one after the other."

Mother Cabrini became still as he continued. "They have suffered under the social instability of that country, I'm afraid." She could tell that Father Terradas was unwilling to go into details in an attempt to allay her fears.

"Where are they? Are they safe?" she asked.

"I was told they had to abandon the school and convent, and have fled. I am sorry I don't have more specific information for you."

They were silent and then Mother Cabrini prayed aloud in a low voice, "May Jesus protect them on their journey and bring them to safety."

That night she barely slept, thinking about her Sisters. Just before dawn, she finally got up and went out onto the deck. As she stepped out, she looked up to see a colorful aurora shimmering in the dawn sky. "With vivid splendors, it lifted our souls…" wrote Mother Cabrini, describing the phenomenon. She took it as a sign of the loving and motherly protection of the Immaculate Mother Mary. "I seem to see her beauty, power, and majesty everywhere," she wrote. "The sea in its immense vastness speaks to me of her. The azure, crystalline waters, reflecting the open book of Mary's virtues."

Mother Cabrini often prayed to Mary Immaculate, and urged her Sisters to do so also whenever they were afraid or doubted themselves. "How beautiful is Mary! How lovable!" she wrote. "This noble creature is the manifestation of God on earth. Through her, God will be known, loved, and adored and blessed in the world. Thus with good reason she is, in an altogether special manner, the tender Mother of the Missionary Sisters of the Sacred Heart, who have as their primary goal the sublime mission of instructing the people, to draw them to the knowledge and love of our divine Redeemer. In the infinite goodness of His Divine Heart, He deigned to call us to such a sublime vocation. What shall we fear, daughters, if Mary Immaculate, God's purest dove, is our Mother, our refuge, our hope, and the cause of our joy?"

Prayer soothed Mother Cabrini, and provided an internal peace when outward circumstances challenged her or when she was physically uncomfortable. And this sea voyage was already difficult. The captain allowed more passengers than the ship could comfortably hold, so there was a constant press of people wherever she went. The heat was thick and stifling. Early on, seven stowaways were discovered and had been turned over to the police when the ship reached Santa Cruz de Tenerife. Still, the captain, a faith-filled man, checked on the Sisters often and did his best to make them comfortable.

The women created their own ritual: Each night after dinner the three women went to the back of the ship and sang "Ave Maris Stella"—"Hail Star of the Sea."

Hail, O star of the ocean,
God's own Mother blest,
Ever sinless Virgin,
Gate of heav'nly rest.

Taking that sweet Ave,
Which from Gabriel came,
Peace confirm within us,
Changing Eve's name.

Break the sinners' fetters,
Make our blindness day,
Chase all evils from us,
For all blessings pray.

Show thyself a Mother,
May the Word divine
Born for us thine Infant
Hear our prayers through thine.

Virgin all excelling,
Mildest of the mild,

Free from guilt preserve us
Meek and undefiled.

Keep our life all spotless,
Make our way secure
Till we find in Jesus,
Joy for evermore.

Praise to God the Father,
Honor to the Son,
In the Holy Spirit,
Be the glory one.

Amen.

After singing this beautiful hymn, the women said their prayers and lingered, gazing meditatively at the water churned by the boat trail off into the sea. After weeks of travel, Mother Cabrini and two young Sisters arrived in Buenos Aires. Reunited with the Sisters there, and her many friends, she felt greatly relieved. To their further delight, the Sisters who had fled the Panama foundation arrived at their doorstep just a week later, safe and sound, and eager to tell the exciting story of their dangerous escape.

The convent was at full capacity. Novices from South America had joined the Missionary Sisters of the Sacred Heart in addition to the Sisters from Panama. Mother Cabrini was overjoyed—Italian immigrants who had settled here were in great need. She immediately understood the next priority: find a well-situated, large building for her growing foundation in Buenos Aires.

Although she was sick with a fever, she set out the next day to explore new possibilities. In a short time, she found a large house that had already been used as a school, and included a chapel. Here she organized supplies for a day school. In a matter of months she also established an orphanage, as well as a school in Rosario, and a school and house of studies in Mercedes, a small town on the edge of the Pampa.

Just a few days after Mother Cabrini and her Sisters had settled into their new Mercedes convent, a little girl knocked on their door—she was selling doves and asked if the Sisters would like to buy them. "The Holy Spirit has come to the school!" said Mother Cabrini to her Sisters when they brought the girl and her doves inside. "Buy these doves, and care for them. They will always remind you that the Holy Spirit is here among you."

With so many experienced and energetic Sisters now installed in these foundations, Mother Cabrini felt the time had come to say goodbye to Buenos Aires, and in August of 1901, she returned to Italy.

Women and men who have the true gift of teaching are rare, but they are able to change the hearts and minds of many young people. "Teachers who educate their pupils sow many grains of mustard seed, which, according to the word of the Divine Master, will grow to an immense height," wrote Mother Cabrini in a letter to students in Rome, "though it may never be allowed to the teachers themselves to know how abundant the fruit will be."

Mother Cabrini's instincts as a teacher made her a beloved leader for her Sisters—those from Italy, and those who joined from other countries. She looked for the innate talents in each Sister so that she could make sure they were able to do their best work. She corrected their faults with steadfast kindness, taught them to put charity and humility in all their work, and always lifted their spirits with her laughter and good humor.

She was as devoted to them as they were devoted to her, and her visits to their foundations were cause for great excitement and celebration. They longed to experience her faith firsthand, and to receive her guidance and wisdom in all their many projects. Her kindness and encouragement kept them going, even when they had few resources.

Though united in their love for *La Madre*, the Missionary Sisters of the Sacred Heart were immersed in very different kinds of care—for orphans, immigrant families, prisoners, school children, hospital patients, people who sought out religious education, and young women without families who badly needed skills.

But education, especially for young women, was of paramount importance to Mother Cabrini and her Sisters. "The greatest heritage of a girl is a good education," she told them. Without education, girls would be vulnerable in the world for their entire lives. Mother Cabrini insisted that girls in her schools and orphanages learn simple skills such as sewing and embroidery. She was so proud of the work they did that she entered it in contests and exhibitions. For this reason, she often allowed orphaned girls to stay on with the Sisters long after they had grown out of adolescence; not surprisingly, many joined the Missionary Sisters of the Sacred Heart.

Girls from well-off families would benefit from education in a different way: It could save them from leading frivolous, inconsequential lives. She believed that all girls should be taught to work, and to keep their bodies as well as their minds strong and active. Mother Cabrini encouraged girls to play games such as tennis and cricket, and go on hikes in the countryside.

Mother Cabrini also believed in bilingual education so that no matter where Italian children went to school, they could learn as quickly as others, and at the same time, maintain their cultural identity.

As a gifted and experienced educator, Mother Cabrini understood the value of teaching literature and science in a way that was meaningful to children, and in an environment where they felt cared for and willing to learn. She wrote a small booklet for all the Sisters who were teachers, instructing them to follow her educational methods, and why she believed in them. They included these suggestions.

- Fashion the hearts of the students to a love of religion and the practice of virtue.
- Safeguard the children confided to you as on precious loan.
- Let your example speak louder than your words.
- Maintain a maternal solicitude for the children.
- Study well the personalities, the strengths of the students, because one cannot presume they are all the same. Treat each one according to their capacity and the gifts they have received from God.
- Seek to form character.
- Do not embarrass; correct patiently.
- Do not show dislike either in words or actions.
- Do not speak of the students' defects to others.
- Use all possible diligence to plan your schoolwork at the beginning of the year. Always be ready to answer to educational authorities and satisfy the families of the students.
- See that the environment is clean and well ordered.

Teaching children, she believed, had a far higher purpose for Italy and the world than simply drilling facts into young minds: "Do not let your teaching be concerned only with literature, science, mathematics, and history," she wrote. "Let your instruction deal also with solid, moral, and religious truths; and you will render a great service, not only to religion, but also to your country. You will make a great contribution to the achievement of the political equality of today for which so many children of Italy are emigrating to foreign lands. You will help to make our country honored and respected among other nations." It is no wonder that the Sisters were continually in demand as teachers by parishes around the country.

Indeed, Mother Cabrini and her Sisters were invited to establish not just schools but also orphanages in cities around the world—and they obliged as much as they could. To pay for all these projects, Mother Cabrini could never let up on her search for money. Her best sources were the wealthy passengers she found on her voyages aboard steam ships and ocean liners. She would make their acquaintance and tell them about her missionary work. Sometimes they would be so moved that they would donate funds on the spot.

And now she was learning that gold had been found in Colorado and other states. Perhaps, she thought with excitement, she and her Sisters could pan for gold! Italians had worked in gold and silver mines—dangerous work that killed or injured many, leaving families destitute. Even small amounts of gold were there to be had by anyone strong and brave enough to look for it. For this reason, she longed to see the western states.

∾

Mother Cabrini sent Sisters to Chicago, Denver, and Seattle, urging them to find Italian immigrant communities that most needed their services. In 1901, she traveled by train across the United States to Denver—where she was transfixed by the soaring, snow-capped Rocky Mountains.

She wrote to her Sisters, "The Diocese of Denver comprises a vast territory since it is the only one in Colorado, a state whose area exceeds that of Italy. One third of it is plains, the remaining two thirds are formed by the mountainous regions of the Rocky Mountains. This is a very high chain of mountains; the highest peak reaches 14,440 feet. As their name well indicates, they are enormous masses of rock tinted with the most attractive colors of the rainbow, making them a charming sight, one of the more beautiful natural regions of the United States.

"Their enormous, painted masses seem to be hanging by a thread. Railroads snake along the slopes to the highest peaks, then descend to the opposite valleys, then course through very narrow gorges called canyons. The canyons' inaccessible walls, radiant colors and artistic forms resemble the walls of an enchanted castle. Anyone seeing their panorama would think it was a creation of the artist's brush."

She and the Sisters first established a small orphanage, but soon realized that Italian immigrants needed much more—most had suffered from years-long separation from their church. Couples had never had their marriages blessed by a priest or their children baptized. Young adults nearing their thirties lacked spiritual values and had never made their First Communion.

"In the mountains, hundreds of workers can be found who have not received the sacraments for many years," she wrote. "They are exhausted from their labors and live far from a church, where Holy Mass is rarely celebrated." Determined to reach the miners, Sisters descended hundreds of feet into the earth to meet the men and remind them of spirituality in the midst of their relentless labor to find gold. And the Sisters saw, firsthand, the harsh working conditions of men who risked their lives, yet earned very little money. The owners of the mining companies, however, were rich. Seeing this, Mother Cabrini realized how much she and her Sisters were needed in these communities, and she vowed to stay as long as she could and to encourage more Sisters in Italy to prepare for missionary work in America.

Father Mariano Lepore, pastor of the local Italian church, asked the Missionary Sisters of the Sacred Heart if they would open a much-needed school, and Mother Cabrini readily agreed. As soon as it was opened, two hundred children were enrolled by their parents. Bishop Matz, who could speak Italian as well as other languages, honored the children with an official visit, giving his blessing and encouragement to them all.

Like all her projects, this school needed support and Father Lepore did all he could to help Mother Cabrini and her sisters expand their school as part of the Mount Carmel mission. A wealthy Italian family—the Cuneos—provided a stove, and Father Lepore made sure water pipes and toilets were installed. But on November 18, 1903, Father Lepore was shot and killed by an Italian immigrant who claimed that the priest owed him money from a venture in Italy. The shooting signaled the beginning of violence between men of several Italian factions in Denver, one of which established another Catholic church named Saint Rocco's as the church for Italians. The Sisters bravely kept up their work in the midst of the violence, doing their best to protect the children. Mother Cabrini intervened and her Mount Carmel parish survived as the parish for Italians. Peace was restored.

Mother Cabrini returned to Denver many times in her life, drawn to its beauty as well as to the needs of its people. As she became familiar with the city and saw it grow, she purchased property for a summer camp for orphans. Later she built a stone house there, made with local rock, and this house was used as a chapel and dormitories for the Sisters and orphans. The only problem was that the only water source was quite a distance from the house.

Just as she had done in West Park, Mother Cabrini walked the property from end to end, and finally pointed to a spot where she believed water could be found. Sure enough, when laborers came to dig there, a spring was discovered that provided more than enough water for the orphans and Sisters.

She was needed in so many places at the same time that Mother Cabrini had to plan her trips wisely. Now she had just arrived in Chicago, after a trip back east to help found an orphanage in Arlington, New Jersey, at the request of Sisters who called attention to the need there. Mother Cabrini had long hoped to establish an orphanage in Chicago. But Archbishop James Edward Quigley, who knew his people very well, informed her that a hospital was more urgently needed, and asked her whether she could change direction.

She agreed, although as usual there was no funding. As was her way, she did not let this stop her—she and her Sisters began their days by going out to beg for money on the street, while also looking for an appropriate building to purchase.

Chicago—right at the edge of the vast Lake Michigan, was a vibrant city that captivated Mother Cabrini. She loved that the wide streets lined with elegant buildings were so close to this windswept lake. One day on her walks, an abandoned six-story, one-hundred-fifty-room building caught her eye. It was the North Shore Hotel, and it was for sale. With Bishop Quigley's blessing, she began negotiations to purchase the hotel and surrounding property. She sensed something was amiss when she examined the papers and then went out and examined the property carefully.

Gathering her Sisters at dawn one morning, she discovered that the sellers were in fact attempting to swindle her out of a significant portion of the land. So she confronted the dishonest businessman in his office, telling him about the surveyor lines that had been moved in his favor.

"I measured the property myself! Are you so unfortunate that you feel emboldened to try to cheat the Missionary Sisters of the Sacred Heart—followers of our savior Jesus Christ?" she asked, looking directly in the eye of the flustered businessman seated at his desk.

"Why, this must be a misunderstanding, Mother. We did not intend to cheat you, not at all!" The man's face turned red, and he would not return her gaze. He hastily signed the purchase agreement, and after a careful reading, Mother Cabrini signed it as well. The two shook hands.

The Columbus Hospital in Chicago was now about to become a reality. Work began immediately to renovate the North Shore Hotel such that it would have the latest equipment to serve the poor as well as patients who could afford to pay for treatment. It would have several operating rooms, an X-ray machine, and a training college for nurses—in other words, it was going to be a first-class hospital.

Mother Cabrini was pleased with the progress of the renovations and left near the end of the project for a trip out of state, returning in February 1905, just before the official opening date. The scene she discovered appalled her.

In her absence, the work had slowed down to a snail's pace. Now a year's worth of work would have to be done in a matter of months to meet the deadline of the grand opening. It was an all-hands-on-deck crisis.

Cabrini fired the architects and contractors and decided to supervise the completion of the project herself. But where would she find workers? She went into the Italian community and hired unemployed men—laborers as well as artists—to finish the work under her close watch. They worked around the clock, with the Sisters pitching in too. During this time, one of the workers, who had been Protestant up until this time, decided to become Catholic—and all work stopped for a short celebration. At last, the building was completed by the date necessary so that the opening could take place as planned.

February 26, 1905, began as a chilly but dazzlingly sunny day for the grand opening celebration of Chicago's Columbus Hospital. The sky was a clear blue and the waters of Lake Michigan sparkled. More than four thousand people crowded the area to celebrate the new hospital and to witness Bishop Quigley give it his blessing. Not one to feel comfortable in the spotlight, Mother Cabrini had to be cajoled into allowing a photographer to take her picture. She did not enjoy the experience. "I hope this is the last one I have taken in my lifetime," she later wrote to a friend. The photo, which exists today, shows her seated formally on what appears to be a leather-backed chair. She sits erect, wearing the black habit of her order, with a large silver cross hanging at her abdomen, her hands folded on her lap. She gazes into the camera with a small, patient smile. Her large eyes are filled with a calm kindness. It is a direct, steady gaze that exudes wisdom and strength.

However, that strength to think and behave independently sometimes offended others. When Cabrini chose an American surgeon of Irish descent, Dr. John B. Murphy, as head of the medical staff, Italian doctors were outspoken in their criticism. Tensions eased when she hired two Italian surgeons, Dr. Camillo Volini and Dr. Antonio Lagorgorio, as staff members. Guido Sabetta, an official of Chicago's Italian Consulate, complained that the hospital did not reserve enough free beds for poor Italians. Mother Cabrini agreed, but reminded him that the hospital was still in its first few years of existence.

Criticism was launched at Mother Cabrini from another quite unexpected direction—a small group of young Sisters in Rome became vocally opposed to some of the rules she had put in place for the Missionary Sisters of the Sacred Heart. They were vocal enough to get the attention of some religious officials.

Mother Cabrini pitied the young women. She wrote to the Superior of the Rome house, "Frivolous and over-imaginative personalities, ill or otherwise, we shall always have; therefore, arm yourself with patience, trying to keep them within bounds as well as you can, sometimes with kindness and sometimes with severity, however you deem it wise…"

And directly to the rebellious Sisters she wrote, "Do you like this family of the Sacred Heart? If you do like it, well, then, continue on with courage. Eradicate your faults and you will become holy. If you do not like the family, it is useless to stay here and harm your sisters, for you cannot be holy. My dear children, do not lose time in vain imaginations; building castles in the air will never enrich you. With one drop of true humility and love for your Spouse, all can be remedied. I forgive you with my whole heart, but I want you to sacrifice yourselves willingly and with the generosity with which you first sacrifice yourselves."

Years later, when Mother Cabrini and another of her Sisters were in Rome, they spotted one of the religious officials who had supported the rebellious Sisters; the two women smiled at him graciously, but he averted his eyes and rushed past them.

She was curious about the young city of Seattle, which had been founded around the time of her own birth. As soon as Mother Cabrini could, she ventured northwest from Denver to explore the area. Surrounded by the Puget Sound and dotted with tall, thousand-year-old trees and snow-covered mountain peaks looming above the horizon on clear days, Seattle's views were spectacular and its air was refreshingly cool.

Italian men had been making their way to Seattle for years, searching for gold or to work in the new lumber industry. The population also swelled with entrepreneurs ready to make money off the most gullible immigrants—selling gophers trained to find gold, for instance. The presence of Mother Cabrini and her Sisters on the street, wearing their veils, long black tunics, and silver crosses, now drew stares. Some men averted their gaze out of an immediate sense of guilt, but others drew closer, as if the sight of the nuns reminded them of their home country and their long-lost religion.

The younger Sisters shrank away from their stares, but Mother Cabrini welcomed them, and often stopped to speak to strangers. She wanted to be known as a friendly presence, and to show the Sisters how to reach out to make the acquaintance of citizens. But she never wanted to be singled out as their leader. "If a stranger should stop us," she told them, "don't address me as Mother, just call me Sister." In this way, she found men who told her they had not been to church in forty or fifty years. To be able to speak their native Italian with the Missionary Sisters of the Sacred Heart thrilled the immigrants, and convinced them to return to church.

"This city is charmingly situated," she wrote, describing Seattle to her Sisters in Italy, "and is growing so rapidly that it will become another New York. Its port is open to the steamers that sail to and from Alaska. The town of Seattle spreads over twenty hills and though it is fifty degrees north latitude, it enjoys an interminable spring because of the current that comes from Japan. It is an excellent place for delicate people; and while I am establishing a house here, I shall be able to take advantage of this superb climate. The bishop is very good. His name is O'Dea, and he is happy to have us in his dioceses because we bear the name of the Sacred Heart of Jesus. He is very much devoted to the Sacred Heart, and is doing everything in his power to spread the devotion." Within a short time, Mother Cabrini and her Sisters established a convent, school, and a chapel in the Beacon Hill section of Seattle.

Bishop Edward J. O'Dea was born of Irish immigrants and his father had come to the American West during the California Gold Rush. O'Dea shared Mother Cabrini's compassion for the many disadvantages that immigrants faced, and he knew firsthand how many Italians in the western states badly needed the Catholic Church, from which they had been separated for so many years.

Indeed, as soon as the Sisters had established their small chapel in Seattle, Italians were eager to see it. "In the beginning, when we did not have a bell, the sisters acted as bells," wrote Mother Cabrini. "Two in one direction and two in the other, they went about the hills gathering those good Italians and hurriedly led them to church. As soon as the first signal is given, you can see them hurrying to church."

As always, Mother Cabrini demonstrated to her Sisters how to muster the courage and strength to start seemingly impossible tasks. When construction work was being done on the Seattle house to expand it a few years later, *La Madre* took up a pick herself to prepare the ground for the foundation. "A true missionary must be able to do any kind of work," she said to the open-mouthed Sisters who watched the petite Mother Cabrini swing the pick into the hard ground.

Instead of retreating to a privileged position within her order, she amazed her Sisters and other religious officials with her energy and willingness to work. She urged the Sisters to tour the neighborhoods of their cities on foot, to find Italian immigrant families, knock on their doors, talk to them, get to know them, and invite them to Mass. When money was needed, she went out to beg with the other Sisters. When cleaning had to be done, she rolled up her sleeves and mopped floors. "I wouldn't want any of my Daughters to undertake any duty that I would refuse to do myself," she said.

~

But the early years of the new century brought painful losses. Mother Cabrini grieved the loss of her old friend, Bishop Corrigan—once an adversary, he became a true friend and supporter when he finally realized just how determined Mother Cabrini really was to help the poor. He had fallen, she learned, and later died of pneumonia, which he had contracted during his convalescence. That had been in May of 1902; he was just sixty-three.

The following month her lovely friend Countess Mary Reid Cesnola died from heart problems. As one of the first patrons in New York for the Missionary Sisters of the Sacred Heart, the Countess and her husband had provided the money that helped Mother Cabrini's first dreams for Italian immigrants in New York City come to fruition. As a result, whole families were able to rise up out of poverty with education, care, and spiritual solace provided by the Sisters.

But the death of Pope Leo XIII in July 1903 reverberated even more deeply in her soul. His kindness had given her the courage to forge ahead in her missionary work. While some men were threatened by her intelligence and independence, Pope Leo XIII respected and admired her. Each time they sat together during her visits to Rome, he listened intently to all she said, and blessed all her adventures.

His pontificate had lasted twenty-five years, and by the end he was revered for how he fought for poor people and laborers to be treated fairly and paid fairly for their work. In Mother Cabrini he saw a woman who believed just as he did, and advocated for the poor around the world. What would she do without him? Maybe this was his final gift to her—showing that she could continue her work even when he departed this earth for Heaven.

Mother Cabrini had to get out and walk. She was never strong physically, but she found that by walking—in fields, among trees, or along streams of rushing water—she was soothed and restored, no matter what troubled her heart. She was perfectly suited to missionary work because she enjoyed traveling, and through her adult life, she rarely stayed in one place for more than a year or two. Walking fed some restless longing deep in her soul—sometimes she felt compelled beyond reason to get out to explore new terrain, new vistas, new worlds.

Walking in cities such as Chicago or New York, amidst bustling crowds of different kinds of people and vendors selling different kinds of trinkets or food—was enjoyable and stimulating. But in the quiet of nature, she felt surrounded by the love and grace of Jesus, and this healed her in body and mind. Now she needed that healing more than ever.

With the recent news of Pope Leo's death weighing heavy on her heart, she stepped out of her Denver mission on a late summer afternoon, and walked to the edge of the city where she found a clear view of the mountains. She prayed as she walked, with the Rocky Mountains as her companions, remembering the three people who had been so critical to her journey as a missionary. They had been so much a part of her life that they felt ever-present, even now. She had always counted on them for support.

The sun was setting. Suddenly, Mother Cabrini did not feel like a Superior General, but like the little girl called Ceccina. She remembered how she used to feel when she was young and played in the fields at home until dinner time, knowing that Rosa would soon be calling for her. Their sister Maddalena had died many years before, and Rosa had moved to Argentina long ago to be with their brother, Giovanni, and then she later died too. After a moment of standing perfectly still before the majestic mountains, she turned to retrace her steps back to the mission. She felt a strange surge of strength, and resolved to honor her friends by redoubling her efforts to restore these far-flung Italians to their faith.

Chapter Fifteen

A CELEBRATION IN CALIFORNIA

Stretching her legs out from her chair in the quiet garden, Mother Cabrini turned her face toward the warm sun. The air was hot and dry, yet it was fragrant with the scent of sage and rosemary bushes. Los Angeles, with its constant sunshine, soothed Mother Cabrini, who badly needed rest. She had worked long hours for many years, often in ill health. Now she was feeling especially tired and welcomed the warmth and quiet. She had been eager to see Los Angeles, which she estimated had a population of about three hundred thousand in 1905, the year of her first visit.

Reflecting on her train trip, she still marveled at one frightening incident. She had been telling her two traveling companions that she had just read in the Denver newspaper that robbers were known to hide in the desert and jump on passenger trains as they slowed before rounding sharp curves. In describing how it was done, she accidentally dropped an apple on the floor that had been on her lap. As she leaned down to pick it up, the glass window next to her seat shattered.

The Sisters screamed, and the conductor came running to their compartment. He examined the window, and then asked

Mother Cabrini to lean to the side as he extracted a bullet from the back of her seat, just next to her head. "It looks to me as if you are mighty lucky, Mother," said the conductor. "If you had not bent down at that moment, you would have been killed with this bullet." The Sisters were upset, but Mother Cabrini sat back and smiled. She knew deep in her heart that she was protected. She had too much work to do to leave this earth now.

Besides, Los Angeles now had her full attention—its landscape was more dramatic than she expected. Jasmine, bougainvillea, orange trees, and eucalyptus created an intoxicating fragrance, and added bright splashes of color and shape to the landscape. She visited the neighborhood called Venice, with small houses lining man-made canals that had been the brainstorm of Abbot Kinney, a tobacco businessman who developed an interest in conservation and real estate. Kinney, like Mother Cabrini, had discovered that the Southern California climate was restorative—here, his asthma disappeared.

The mountains in Los Angeles were low compared to the peaks Mother Cabrini had admired in Seattle, but beautiful in their own way. These were covered with yucca and other cacti, and rocks of all colors. She had seen wild rabbits and coyotes darting in the brush, stopping to stare at her, unafraid.

This was certainly a hot, dusty city, but the warmth lifted her spirits. "The climate is excellent, so I recuperate while I'm working," she wrote to her Sisters in Italy. She could breathe deeply here, without the dreaded fits of coughing. She needed to be strong because there was much work to be done. For more than thirty years poor Italians in Los Angeles had been without a priest who spoke their language. As a consequence, some had turned to the Protestant churches…the ultimate disaster, in Mother Cabrini's view.

After sending two Sisters ahead to find rooms to rent, Mother had arrived in Los Angeles by train in July of 1905. From her seat on the train, she noticed Italian men working in the hot sun on the railroad lines along mountain sides, and realized that here, as everywhere, Italians were relegated to the most difficult, physically demanding work—and probably with no break for weeks on end.

Bishop Thomas Conaty of Los Angeles had invited her to come, hoping she would bring teachers for his schools. But upon arrival, Cabrini quickly saw more was needed. For weeks, she and her Sisters rose early each morning to explore different neighborhoods of the city, learning the names of streets and hills, and getting to know the nationalities and needs of people who lived there.

This was the way in which she began every new establishment. One Sister later wrote about her, "When she was about to start a new foundation, she would first of all study the country. She would be out from morning until night, studying the land very carefully in every direction until she knew almost every inch of it. When she had done this and had acquired all the information that might be useful by listening with prudence and consideration to the opinions of others—she never despised any comment and was always ready to learn—then from the various opinions she made her own judgment."

By November, they had found a house to purchase at Sunset Boulevard and Hill Street—and *La Madre* could not have been more pleased with the choice. "There is no house, no matter how small, that does not have its little flower garden," she wrote to one of her Missionary Sisters, describing Los Angeles. "The palm trees give the whole city an aspect of elegance. Exactly on one of these hills, I found the right place for our house. I can indeed say that the Sacred Heart prepared it for us, because the large garden filled with palm trees in front of the house hide it from view so that it is a true convent. At the same time, we are a short distance from the center of the city. At the foot of our hill are the houses of our Italians, so that in a few minutes the Sisters can be about their mission and go to the school which Bishop Conaty is building for us."

She named the building Regina Coeli—Queen of Heaven—Orphanage, and they were soon able to take in Italian and Mexican girls. A few years later, so many girls lived there that Mother Cabrini realized that the orphanage needed to expand. With little money, she did not see how this could happen, until one day she passed a sign advertising the sale of wood from a house being torn down. Neighborhood children pitched in to help as she loaded carts with the wood and made dozens of trips to bring it to the orphanage. A Sister from Italy came to oversee the construction of the new building—and enough wood was left over that Mother Cabrini had it sent to Denver for her foundation there.

Wherever she traveled, Mother Cabrini was an enthusiastic tourist, and she especially enjoyed nature. Los Angeles offered plenty for her to explore by foot, by horse and buggy, and by boat. When one of the two Banning brothers, who owned Catalina Island just off the southern coast of Los Angeles, got word of Mother Cabrini's presence in Los Angeles, he invited her to visit their island. She responded that she would be most grateful for the opportunity to see his island. He met her at the dock on a brisk Saturday morning and helped her onto the small boat with about a dozen other passengers. As they crossed the channel, the passengers were treated to a display of dolphins leaping out of the water close to the boat, then playfully swimming under it. Mother Cabrini was thrilled—and tried to soak up every detail so that she could relay it to her Sisters later.

"I went there on a beautiful day when the sky was cobalt blue and the ocean justified its name," she wrote to them the next day. "The three hours of the crossing passed swiftly in the contemplation of the immense ocean with nothing but sky and water in sight. As we drew near the bay that makes up the small port, a translucent mist extended like a veil in front of the immense, thirty-mile-long mass of rock that forms the island, letting us see only its outline. When we drew closer, this great curtain lifted gently as in a magnificent theater prepared by nature. I assure you I seemed to be dreaming, transported to an earthly paradise."

Another aspect of California that she found fascinating, and somewhat distressing, were the many religious sects with strange practices—some of them meeting in public places for all to see. Faith healers, Nazarenes, Christian Scientists, and smaller groups led by individual preachers all seemed to find willing followers. She had seen this with her own eyes.

As she walked along the street one evening with Sister Josephina Becci on the way home to their convent, they saw a crowd gathered. Pushing through to see what the crowd was looking at, they saw a dozen men and women thrashing about on the sidewalk. The people kicked their feet, pulled at their own clothes, and even slapped themselves, as if in a kind of insane fit. A man calling himself a preacher stood by, shouting that they had sinned and must show their sorrow and repent.

Mother Cabrini and Sister Josephina were about to turn away to get back to the convent, when a well-dressed gentleman leaned over to them.

"Don't leave yet," he said with a wink. "You'll miss the best part!"

All of a sudden, the men and women leapt up and began dancing about, clapping their hands and shouting in a delirious joy. Surely the two nuns had never seen such a bizarre sight in their lives.

"They are called Holy Jumpers," explained the gentleman to Sister Josephina, who translated for Mother Cabrini. "They just now believed that all their sins have been pardoned and so they are celebrating. They are a curious group, somewhat radical. They are against owning property and they're suspicious of most religions."

Mother Cabrini shook her head in wonder. The gentleman introduced himself as Mr. Steven Huber, and asked if he could walk the two women to the convent to make sure they were safe. They thanked him and said, yes, that would be very kind.

"Obviously, you are not from here," he said as they strolled together. "What do you think of Los Angeles?"

"I like the city very much—it is quite beautiful," said Mother Cabrini. "I have never known a place where flowers seem to grow everywhere, with little tending. But those people we just saw, that is disturbing."

"Indeed. But some are worse—they demand money from their followers, who are so poor they can barely get by," he said.

"I saw one scene that was like that," Mother Cabrini recalled. "There was a big tent and a man shouting that he could cure the sick and make the blind see. An old man who had a hunched back and a bad limp hobbled up to the tent, and the man shouted, 'Lord, listen to us, this believer wants to walk straight. Help him, Lord, cure him now!' But of course, the man could not walk straight, so he was hustled out the back of the tent!"

"Charlatans everywhere take advantage of the poor, that is certain," said the gentleman. "The pity is that many call themselves Christians."

As they now had reached the convent, Mr. Huber said goodnight to Mother Cabrini and Sister Josephina, and as the two nuns opened the convent door, he walked off into the warm night.

Bishop Conaty surprised Mother Cabrini with a gala celebration and Mass to mark the twenty-fifth anniversary of the founding of the Missionary Sisters of the Sacred Heart in Italy. Catholic Angelenos were ecstatic that Cabrini was in their city on this occasion, which drew attention to all that she had accomplished by age fifty-five. By now, her name was well known from coast to coast in America, and her work was reported not just in religious papers but in the secular press too. "We were always hidden until now. Now everyone is interested in us," she said to her Sisters, with a hint of dismay.

Once the Los Angeles foundation was established, Mother Cabrini traveled to Chicago and was pleased to find that her Columbus Hospital, under the direction of Dr. Murphy, was thriving. It was now caring for approximately nine hundred patients, only a fraction of whom were Italian. But a new need was becoming apparent—a hospital exclusively for poor Italians. Dr. Camillo Volini, the Chicago hospital's chief of staff, warned Mother Cabrini that life-threatening errors could occur in the hospital when patients could not describe their symptoms nor understand the doctors who prescribed treatment.

"We need a hospital where the poor people not only receive aid for their maladies, but the kindness and attention that can come only from a compatriot," he said. Mother Antonietta

Della Casa, who now was president of the Missionary Sisters of the Sacred Heart, made an official request for the new hospital, and noted that the Archbishop of Chicago saw this as an urgent need. The Sisters set about locating a large building for the Columbus Extension Hospital, and Mother Cabrini began soliciting donations from wealthy patrons, Italian groups, and the general public.

But Mother Cabrini had seen many opportunities on the West Coast, and yearned to go back to the warm climate of Los Angeles, which she did the following year. The dry air of Southern California had eased so much of her respiratory distress, it would surely benefit children whose lungs were weak, she thought. So she purchased 120 acres covered with grape vines and an olive tree orchard in nearby Burbank, where she built a home for children who were weak or suffered from tuberculosis. She and the other Sisters brought groups of children on hikes in the rugged hills, where she especially loved to walk when the sun was setting and the temperatures were cool.

On one such hike she led several Sisters and ten children up a small hill on a path that wound around clumps of trees and large boulders. A red-headed eight-year-old boy named Fabrizio marched close to *La Madre*, chatting with her amiably. "When you were little, where did you live?" he asked her.

"I lived in a little town in Italy, where my parents had a farm," Mother Cabrini replied.

"My mother was from Italy too, but she died. Did you like Italy? My mother said it was beautiful."

"*Si, si*, I liked it very much," said Mother Cabrini. "I was allowed to wander wherever I wanted, and I liked to climb trees."

"My mother said the people there were nice," said the boy, "but now I think I like America."

Mother Cabrini turned to look at this skinny little boy closely—he was an orphan, and clearly did not have a memory of Italy himself, but clung to the memories that his mother had shared with him before she died. "I like America too," she said to him gently.

Fabrizio prattled on. "When I grow up, I want to sell oranges and grapefruit," he said. "Have you seen how many are growing on trees? I could pick them all, put them in a box, and sell them right on the street. I could make lots of money!"

Mother Cabrini laughed. "I hope that you can do that, and much more, Fabrizio." She marveled at this child—already thinking like an entrepreneur—who would grow up as an American. What would his life be like here? Where would his path take him? Would he ever see Italy? She silently prayed for his safety, and for a prosperous life ahead.

Because it was a quiet, peaceful place, the Sisters soon brought orphans to the Burbank home from other parts of Los Angeles every summer to give them a respite from city life. Many years later, this site would become Villa Cabrini Academy for girls, then Woodbury University. The Villa Cabrini chapel is a library today.

Chapter Sixteen

DISEASE AND FEAR

It was time to tell Mother Cabrini what was happening. Mother Josephine Lombardi, the local superior in New Orleans, sat down at her small wooden table to write a letter to *La Madre*, who was in Denver. But she did not know quite how to begin. The ceiling fan whirred, and she wiped her brow with a kerchief. The air was thick and stifling.

How could she describe the disaster that was unfolding in New Orleans?

Simply put, a new outbreak of yellow fever, which had begun in the Italian community, was quickly spreading. Men, women, and children of all ages were coming down with fevers, chills, and headaches. Some of them began to turn yellow. Anyone in New Orleans who had lived through previous epidemics recognized the symptoms immediately. Mother Lombardi reminded Mother Cabrini that scientists had determined that the illness is borne by mosquitoes—blood-feeding insects that could transmit the disease.

Yet, false notions about yellow fever swirled about New Orleans. Scientists determined that standing pools of water were the perfect breeding ground for mosquitoes, but some people firmly believed that mosquitoes laid eggs in the ground, which was why men could be seen digging up open areas of earth and then carting it away.

Mother Lombardi put her pen to paper to write: One primary feature of New Orleans, she explained to Mother Cabrini, is the large aboveground cisterns designed to catch rainwater to use as drinking water—and this seemed to be the culprit in the outbreak, along with the fact that New Orleans was built on a swamp. But most urgent in Mother Lombardi's mind was how to explain the abject terror that was seizing the citizens of New Orleans. It was not without good reason: During previous epidemics of yellow fever in the 1850s, tens of thousands of people died. And how to describe the Missionary Sisters of the Sacred Heart who bravely put themselves at risk by going into the homes of sick and dying people to give food and comfort?

A knock on the door interrupted Mother Lombardi's train of thought.

"Come in!" she said. In burst a young Sister Sylvia Barsotti.

"Mother Lombardi! I have just heard the most frightening words—I was in the market when I mentioned to another person that I hoped the schools would close soon to protect the children from contracting yellow fever, when a man turned and said to me, 'Be very careful. If you even say the words yellow fever, they will shoot you!'"

The Sister burst into tears as Mother Lombardi hugged her, patting her on the back. "You are quite right about the schools," said the older woman, "but no one will shoot you for telling the truth about what is happening. The city officials are only making matters worse by pretending the fever is not spreading here again—but it most certainly is!"

"Mother, the families who are the most stricken are the ones whose men work at the docks, unloading crates of fruit from the ships." Mother Lombardi stared at the young nun, realizing that this must be the way the disease was spreading.

"I will tell this to the health officials today," she said.

But several weeks later, she wrote again to Mother Cabrini with new terrible news. Italian families were refusing to see the Sisters, as well as doctors and health officials, believing that they were actually spreading the yellow fever by visiting so many sick people. Nevertheless, the Sisters continued their visits as best as they could, caring for the families and winning them over by bringing food and comforting the sickest ones.

Desperately sad scenes were unfolding in these homes— where parents were dying or lying dead in their beds, surrounded by their helpless small children. The Sisters gathered the children to take them to their convent. And some patients refused medicine. In an attempt to convince them that the medicine was safe, Sisters would sometimes swallow it to show that it was not poison. When the city of New Orleans used fumigation to get rid of mosquitoes, some Italians feared that was poison too, so the Sisters allowed their convent to be fumigated repeatedly to prove that it did not kill human beings.

The Sisters worked closely with officials from the Department of Health—and visited families who would allow no one else in their homes. They sat with the dying, and accompanied some patients to the hospital to make sure they were comfortable and felt safe. Mother Cabrini understood the severity of the situation, and appealed to the Italian Commissioner of Emigration, Leone Reynaudi, for money to support the poorest Italian families in New Orleans. When the epidemic subsided, it left a population even more debilitated than before.

The bravery and invaluable help provided by the Missionary Sisters of the Sacred Heart during the epidemic of 1905 were recognized by the Italian Minister of Foreign Affairs, Pope Pius X, and other local officials. Mother Cabrini, reading about the accolades in a letter from Mother Lombardi, could not have been more proud.

Chapter Seventeen

TROUBLE IN RIO

At the end of four years spent exclusively in America, Mother Cabrini returned to Italy to visit the Sisters in each of her Italian foundations. Soon after, she planned a long voyage to see the Sisters in the Buenos Aires foundation. The relationship between Italy and Argentina had deteriorated since her last visit. Argentina had welcomed Italian immigrants for many years—they were a significant factor in boosting the Argentinian economy. Also, the Italian government had encouraged its citizens to go to Argentina, as a kind of sister country. But the immigrants eventually found that in Argentina they were mistreated just as they were in America. As the Argentinian economy began to founder, many immigrants decided to return to their homeland.

Now, a fear of cholera led the Argentinian authorities to require quarantines and health inspections of boats arriving to its shores from Italy. Indignant and offended, Italians complained that these rules were unnecessary—after all, the number of days it took to travel from Italy to Argentina should be enough of a quarantine period.

Into this atmosphere Mother Cabrini arrived in Buenos Aires, with the intention of finding new, larger quarters for her foundations. But when that proved difficult, she shifted her focus to visiting Sisters in São Paulo, who had started a house there a few years before. Hearing that she was in Brazil, Cardinal Arcoverde invited her to open a foundation in Rio de Janeiro. As soon as he could, the Cardinal Archbishop made his way to the street where Mother Cabrini had purchased the building for her foundation. Hurrying down the street, at last he found the correct address and, seeing that the door was open, stepped inside the foyer. In the dim light, a woman was cleaning the floor.

"Pardon me, I am looking for Mother Frances Cabrini—can you tell me where I might find her here?" he asked the woman, speaking slowly in case she did not understand him.

"Yes, you will find her in the next room," said the cleaning woman. "Please, I will let her know you are here and she will be there in a few minutes."

The Cardinal found his way into the sitting room and stood uncomfortably near the door. Suddenly, another door flew open from the opposite side, and in swept Mother Cabrini—and he realized immediately that she was the cleaning woman he had seen just minutes before.

She bowed and then cordially invited Cardinal Arcoverde to be seated, smiling mischievously. "It is a pleasure to meet you at last!" he said with flourish, and a hint of irony. "I welcome you to our city, and I am at your service—to help you do all you can for our people." Mother Cabrini nodded respectfully, as he continued. He leaned forward in his chair, and his demeanor lost all levity. "The situation is difficult," he said. "I would like to explain what has been taking place in Rio these last few years."

Rio's population was rapidly growing, he said, with immigrants from Spain, Portugal, and Italy, as well as former slaves from within the country pouring in to the city. There was much turmoil—yellow fever, the plague, and smallpox were killing large numbers of people. Just recently, the director of public health had ordered mosquito fumigations and all pools of water to be drained. Unclean houses were to be demolished as well. But, said the Cardinal, when the director called for mandatory vaccinations against smallpox, people revolted—and massive protests erupted around the city. Citizens were suspicious of the government's motives. Riots led to destruction of property and several deaths. The government repealed the mandatory smallpox vaccination, and peace was restored.

"We all fear these deadly diseases," he said. Mother Cabrini listened intently. She would need to protect her Sisters in their work here, that was clear, although she wasn't quite sure how.

The Rio house for the Missionary Sisters of the Sacred Heart was at last completed. Only one last step was required—an inspection by local health officials. Days before this was to take place, one of the nuns from São Paulo—Sister Gesuina Marinoni—fell ill with the dreaded smallpox. She suffered fever, aches, and sores that covered her body. Soon another nun fell ill with the same symptoms, and then another. Hoping to keep the opening on schedule and to prevent the disease from spreading, Mother Cabrini immediately moved the nuns to a small cottage, and stayed with them to give comfort as they became more and more ill. But when word got out about the nuns' smallpox, local residents protested the presence of the Missionary Sisters in Rio, and questioned whether or not their foundation should open as planned.

In a short time Sister Gesuina died, followed by the other two nuns. Grieving for these Sisters who wanted so much to be part of the new foundations in Brazil, Mother Cabrini bristled when their efforts were criticized. But to prevent more smallpox, she opened a small residence in the countryside where students could attend without fear of the disease. It was a bittersweet day when the foundation for the Missionary Sisters of the Sacred Heart did finally open. Wealthy families from São Paulo contributed to the mission, and it was soon well established.

Before she left Brazil, Mother Cabrini made a last visit to an open-air market to purchase supplies. Turning a corner, she bumped into a young woman she recognized instantly. She was one of the local residents who had gossiped about the Sisters just months before and had lobbied for them to depart. The woman flushed at the sight of Mother Cabrini, then quickly offered a superficial word of condolence for the death of Sister Gesuina and the other nuns. Loathing pretense almost more than anything else, Mother Cabrini saw the insincere gesture for what it was and reacted angrily.

"*Come osi!* How dare you approach me!" said Mother Cabrini in a low tone. The woman's eyes widened in fear, and she took a step back. "You pretend to offer condolences, when I know what you have said about me, about the Sisters and all the good work we try so hard to do." The woman glanced about, now desperately wishing to sidestep this confrontation.

"Some people want to ruin the missionary work of the Sacred Heart," said Mother Cabrini, "but they had better beware because the Lord does not pay only on the Sabbath." The young woman turned and hurried away.

Reflecting on Mother Cabrini's strength of character, Cardinal Arcoverde later remarked, "When this extraordinary woman had finished her mission in Rio, where she left two excellent foundations, she might have said with Caesar, 'I came, I saw, I conquered: Veni, Vidi, Vici!'" What neither of them knew was that Mother Cabrini, while in Brazil, had contracted malaria.

Chapter Eighteen

BECOMING AN AMERICAN

Not being a citizen of the United States was a problem. Mother Cabrini had to work with banks, lawyers, and businessmen in her real estate dealings, and it was now obvious that legal transactions would be faster and less complicated if she were an American citizen. She loved Italy and thought of herself as Italian—in fact, she never really was able to learn English. But Mother Cabrini was eminently practical, and applying for US citizenship was an important business step in getting her establishments up and running as quickly as possible. And, like the immigrants for whom she advocated with such passion, she had fallen in love with America.

On October 9, 1909, in Seattle, with the help of her lawyer, Mother Cabrini became a citizen of the United States. She had returned to the Pacific Northwest earlier that summer to attend the much talked-about Alaska-Yukon Exposition—a world's fair that would include a Women's Building to showcase charity work. Embroidery and other needlework done by her orphans would be on display at the Exposition, so *La Madre* arranged for the girls to be brought there to see it.

The Exposition was well publicized—railroad lines promoted travel across the country to see it and newspapers covered the exciting upcoming events regularly. On opening day, approximately eighty thousand people arrived at the entrance gate. When it closed four months later, the Exposition had hosted more than three million visitors.

Taking the children to the Exposition was just one example of how Mother Cabrini and her Sisters always worked to engage the orphans in the world around them. They took them on summer outings and put on festive holiday parties for them. Sympathetic neighbors donated food and supplies for the children, whose numbers at the orphanage were growing.

At this time eighty-five children were in the Sisters' care and they took in more each month. Soon they learned that they would need to relocate because of a drastic city plan to level the hill on which the orphanage stood. Just as it had happened in West Park years ago, a dream came to *La Madre* in which she saw the details of a new, larger location. So, when she listened as the Sisters excitedly described a summer home for sale right on Lake Washington, she knew immediately it was the right spot—the details matched the house that had appeared in her dream. Once again, a foundation was expanding, and Mother Cabrini's deep instinct was leading the way.

It was 1910, she was nearing her sixtieth birthday, and although she would not mention it to anyone, Mother Cabrini was very, very tired. Even the smallest task fatigued her to the point where she needed to lie down. She had come to Italy once again, in hopes of visiting each of her foundations and meeting with as many Sisters as she could.

But after many days of meditation and reflection, she told them that she wished to step down as Superior General of the Missionary Sisters of the Sacred Heart. The Sisters countered that no one could possibly take her place, so they discussed the matter at length and came up with a solution: They would make a formal request to the Vatican that Mother Cabrini be named General for Life. In spite of her protests, Mother Cabrini received this title on July 6, 1910. Though tired, she had little time to rest—there was too much work to be done. Her schools, orphanages, and hospitals all over the world needed attention. After several years in Italy, she felt the call to return to America—with all her establishments continually growing, she was determined to guide them as best as she could. She was eager to return.

In the spring of 1912, though she certainly did not know it at the time, Cabrini made her last journey from Italy to America. On nearly all of her ocean voyages, she traveled second class in order to be close to the poor Italians, and also because she was frugal by nature. But this time she was so ill that her Sisters made plans for her to travel first class—and they were excited to tell her she would be on the very modern British ship called the *Titanic*.

Mother Cabrini did not want to disappoint the Sisters who had made such a thoughtful plan, but a business emergency at the New York Columbus Hospital forced her to change her travel dates and take a different ship. She voyaged to New York in March instead of April of 1915—and thus was spared an almost certain death by drowning. Just a month later, the *Titanic* struck an iceberg and sank; more than 1,500 people died in the disaster, including the ship's commander and architect.

≈

She could not ignore the fact that her nemesis, the Protestant Church, was again attracting Italians—this time to Philadelphia, where approximately three thousand immigrants from Southern Italy had come to live. Father Peitro Michetti, pastor of the new Saint Donato Parish, asked *La Madre* to come and do what she could to help bring Italians back to the Catholic Church, where they belonged. She negotiated to buy a house near Saint Donato, getting a reduction in the price. She brought five Sisters to Philadelphia to start what would be an elementary school. Soon after that, she purchased another building for an orphanage.

The stress of managing all her foundations took a toll on her body and her spirit. Some property negotiations were fraught with conflicts, and Mother Cabrini had to call on every ounce of her determination and patience to see them through. Also, in New York City a movement was afoot to close down orphanages in the belief that children were not well cared for in such institutions and should be sent to live in family homes. The Missionary Sisters were distraught at this prospect and felt that they and other Catholic institutions were being attacked unfairly. The effort failed, but the episode exhausted *La Madre* and she wondered how much longer she could keep up this intense work.

When she decided to purchase the large Perry Hotel in Seattle so that she could establish a hospital, local residents immediately opposed it, complaining that they did not want a hospital in that part of the city. The Missionary Sisters who lived there suspected the real motives for the opposition: that these men disliked the idea of an establishment being run by an Italian or by a woman.

Most painful to Mother Cabrini was that her dear friend Bishop O'Dea sided with people who were against her. When visiting the Perry Hotel to look it over, he was so angry at her that he pounded his walking stick on a table, insisting she give up on her idea. This upset the usually calm *Madre*, and she began to wonder if this was an effort worth fighting for.

But she patiently met with the city and religious leaders again and again to address their concerns until finally she agreed to a compromise. She would establish a sanitarium instead, a place where patients with long-term illnesses could reside. At last, the contract was ready to be signed, and Bishop O'Dea expressed his apologies for being so difficult and resistant. A telling moment in the final meeting was described this way by one of the nuns:

"Our Mother Foundress, Mother Antoinette, and Mother Paul went together to conclude the contract. The asking price was $190,000. When we arrived at the office of Mr. Chilberg—the bank head who had voluntarily offered to help our Mother—two of the lawyers were whispering, 'Will she have the money?' They were convinced that Mother did not know how to transact business of this kind. But when Mother offered a check of $90,000 and Mr. Chilberg gave a loan of $100,000, they all seemed stupefied. Mother, smiling and speaking in a low tone of voice to the two sisters, said, 'Poor things, they cannot believe that we are able to do a little business.'"

Chapter Nineteen

A QUIET DEATH

In the fall of 1916, feeling weaker than ever before, Mother Cabrini traveled by train from Seattle to Los Angeles, where she hoped the warm weather would rejuvenate her. More often now, she needed to rest several times during the day, so her friend Mother Rita Zamproni agreed to accompany her on all her travels to make sure she was comfortable and able to get the food she needed.

The two women now spent hours in the convent garden in Burbank, soothed by the dry air, exotic flowering plants, and constant chirping of birds. *La Madre* found peace and quiet with the Sisters there and enjoyed the happy exchanges with the children of the orphanage, yet she was also restless to return to the Chicago hospital, which needed constant managing.

The Sisters in Los Angeles worried about *La Madre*. Her face was often clouded with pain, and her usually animated conversation was less frequent. They checked on her constantly, and prayed for her health. Mother Cabrini was deeply upset by the reports she read in the newspaper about details of the Great War that raged in Europe. Hundreds of thousands of Italians—soldiers and civilians—were being killed, and many more wounded. Mother Cabrini wanted badly to travel to Italy, but right now it was just too dangerous.

She would have to be content with going to Chicago, where she was needed. The Sisters understood quite well that no one could keep her from making the trip. Was she strong enough to keep up this pace of travel much longer? She herself did not know. At last, she and Mother Zamproni packed their bags, said their goodbyes to the Los Angeles Sisters, and boarded the train for Chicago in the spring of 1917.

The Sisters who greeted her at the Chicago station were shocked—their beloved leader was obviously slower and weaker than they had ever seen her. Mother Antonietta Della Casa and Mother Grace, head of the Institute in America, both insisted that she allow a doctor to examine her immediately.

The doctors at Columbus Hospital treated her with deferential kindness. They diagnosed her symptoms as malaria, which she had most likely contracted on her last visit to Brazil years earlier. But the treatment they prescribed now left her even more drained. Still, she would not simply sit in a chair or lie in bed all day. When prominent men—Archbishop Giovanni Bonzano, who had been appointed Apostolic Delegate to the United States by Pope Pius X; Cardinal Bonaventura Cerretti; as well as Archbishop Mundelein of Chicago—wrote to say they wished to visit her at the Columbus Hospital, *La Madre* worked diligently to organize a proper celebration to ensure they were received with great fanfare and warmth.

Soon after that, Francesco Saverio Nitti, head of the Italian economic mission to the United States, along with several other politicians, visited Mother Cabrini, who gave them a complete tour of the hospital. It was always wise, she knew, to treat such men graciously, for they may be a source of influence and funding one day. Yet these visits exhausted her—she needed to spend days in bed afterward to recuperate.

When she could, she and Mother Zamproni drove out along country roads in the afternoons, where they stopped to pick flowers to bring back to the hospital chapel. Mother Cabrini always felt renewed by immersing herself in nature, and on one of these drives they passed a small working farm, which gave her an idea.

The next day, when Sister Joanne Morici brought her lunch, *La Madre* turned to her and said, "My dear, will you inquire about farms that are for sale outside of the city as soon as you can? I feel we need to expand, to find a country house where patients can convalesce—and where we might be able to grow our own vegetables and even keep some cows for milk."

"Yes, *La Madre*, I will see what I can find out. And may I ask—what are your wishes for this place?"

"You are kind to ask, Sister. I will tell you," said Mother Cabrini, glancing again out the window. "In truth, I sometimes long for the farm life that I once had as a child. And I now see the usefulness of a small farm where we can create a pleasant location in a quiet setting—a community of Sisters and patients from this hospital who are not well enough to go home."

"I will find this place, *La Madre*. Your dream will be made real," said Sister Morici. She looked at Mother Cabrini—it was painfully clear that the Superior General was weakening. Was she going to pull through this malaria?

Within several weeks, the Sisters found and purchased a farm outside Chicago with *La Madre*'s blessing. They brought her out to see it, and she was delighted to find that it was exactly as she had envisioned: a small stone farmhouse surrounded by trees, with fields nearby that could easily be planted with small crops of produce. She asked the Sisters to inquire about purchasing chickens, cows, and horses too. As she slowly walked around the property, Mother Cabrini mentally planned all the right spots for the gardens and where she could plant fruit trees.

But she privately grieved—she wanted to take a shovel right then and start digging. Tired to the bone, she knew that she was far too weak to do any of this work herself. The next morning, as she went for communion at the end of Mass, she swayed slightly, once again hearing the sound of rushing water around her. Confused, she thought for a minute that she had fallen into a stream. She reached out to grasp something that was not there, and sensing the water closing over her, she fainted. Immediately, her Daughters ran to her, gently lifted her up, and carried her back to her room.

Her activities from then on had to be simple and confined to indoors. During Advent, as Christmas approached, Mother Cabrini spent her days reading in the drawing room or conducting the business of the hospital with her Daughters. On December 8—the Feast of the Immaculate Conception—they gathered to celebrate and play little word games.

She decided that all the Sisters should receive new habits as a Christmas gift. She also bought small gifts for all the doctors and nurses at the hospital, and when she learned that the school for five hundred Italian children could not afford candy, she insisted the Sisters buy the candy at her expense. "They must have candy for Christmas!" she said.

She was happy to participate in the holiday activities at the orphanage and with patients in the hospital as much as her strength would allow. The children, always comfortable with *La Madre*, brought her little gifts and cards—"*La Madre...buon Natale!*"—and draped themselves across her lap to hear the stories she read to them. When the Sisters tried to pull them away, Mother Cabrini said, "No, let them stay with me if they wish. Their sweetness gives me strength."

She also continued to visit the hospital to oversee its daily business, and retreated to her room after these rounds for much-needed rest. One morning, Mother Antonietta and several other Sisters sat at her bedside, going over house matters and reading her stories in the newspaper about the most recent events of the war, staying with *La Madre* for several hours. Before leaving, they asked what she wished to have for lunch, but Mother Cabrini would not say, seemingly uninterested in food. Nevertheless, a small meal was ordered.

At noon, Mother Antonietta returned to Mother Cabrini's room, but finding the door closed, she assumed *La Madre* was getting dressed, and went away. A young Sister carrying a lunch tray arrived and, after tapping gently on the door and hearing no reply, pushed it open—and gasped. Mother Cabrini sat slumped in her chair, her head thrown back at an unnatural angle. Her nightgown was spattered with spots of blood. Crying out, the young Sister ran to get others. Hearing the alarm, Mother Antonietta raced to *La Madre* and tried to revive her with smelling salts. After two almost imperceptible sighs, Mother Cabrini's breathing stopped. Mother Antonietta shouted for a priest and doctors to be called, and gently lifted *La Madre*'s head, cradling the beloved leader in her arms.

Soon the room was filled with distraught Sisters who threw themselves on the floor at the feet of Mother Cabrini, wailing and praying loudly for her soul. "Our most dearly beloved Mother has flown to heaven," said Mother Antonietta. It was December 22, 1917. Mother Cabrini was just sixty-seven years old.

The Sisters placed *La Madre* on her bed and decided to dress her in the new habit that she had ordered for herself as well as all the others for Christmas. A telegram was sent to each of her houses around the country and the world with the simple words: "Mother has flown to heaven."

Her body, which lay in state until December 26, was surrounded with flowers. Thousands of people came to pay their respects. The body was divided—her head was sent to Rome, her heart went to Codogno, an arm remained in Chicago, and the rest of her body was placed in a bronze coffin and carried to the chapel, where the Requiem was celebrated. When at last the coffin was closed, sixteen Sisters prepared to accompany it by train to West Park, New York. Upon their arrival in New York City, they were warmly greeted by priests and other Missionary Sisters of the Sacred Heart. Monsignor Bonzano arrived from Washington and celebrated Mass on Sunday, December 30, 1917, in New York City.

Funeral eulogies were read in Italian and in English, and the final blessing was given by Monsignor Bonzano. The next day *La Madre*'s remains were taken to West Park. One hundred orphans, dressed in white and each carrying a lily, came to pay their respects, and walked with the many grieving Missionary Sisters to the chapel of the convent cemetery, where *La Madre* was laid to rest. It was a cold, snowy day in the New York countryside bounded on one side by the Hudson River, a place that Mother Cabrini loved very much, and where she felt most at peace.

Chapter Twenty

SAINTHOOD

Frances Xavier Cabrini would not have liked to be called a saint. She never wanted accolades or celebrations on her behalf and never called attention to her accomplishments. Yet in her lifetime she established sixty-seven institutions, including schools, colleges, orphanages, hospitals, rest homes, and training schools for nurses. This is especially notable given that the only language she fully understood was Italian. Physically frail and suffering bouts of illness all her life, she nevertheless made twenty-three ocean voyages and even crossed the Andes on foot and on a mule.

But the stories of her warmth and generosity reveal her true gifts. By all accounts, Mother Cabrini was kind and caring toward strangers and friends alike, and provided loving reassurance to Italians who were in trouble and afraid, as well as those who had not seen a priest in years.

Among those who were lucky to know her, she was deeply admired and trusted. "You could always tell her everything," said one of her Sisters after she died. "Even if you didn't confide in her, she seemed to sense your problems. She took a personal interest in everyone." Another Sister remembered that on a ship to Buenos Aires, Mother Cabrini met an old man who was blind, a lawyer who at one time had been quite wealthy, and the two enjoyed speaking every day of the journey. Later, Mother Cabrini learned that the man had been forced to go to a home for the poor and she sought him out. She began to visit him regularly, bringing gifts. The man saved letters he had received from friends and family in Europe, only opening them when Cabrini visited. "You read them to me, Mother," he told her. "I don't trust anyone else."

She was unpretentious and insisted on a life of simplicity, working only to meet the needs of others, particularly the poor and vulnerable. When she experienced difficulty in her work, or physical discomfort, she rarely showed it. Mother Lombardi described her this way: "I found myself with Mother in moments of great difficulty and I always noticed two things: to know that she was suffering you really had to know her because outwardly she remained calm and serene, but she felt misunderstandings very keenly to the depths of her soul; secondly, she had an indescribable courage and energy. One could clearly perceive that Mother saw her road pointed out by God's will." Her faith, which informed her business dealings, played a major part in her ability to envision and then establish and maintain missions that thrived and endured.

She could not tolerate deceit or falseness, and did not hold back her anger when she encountered it in anyone. In business, she was astute and steadfast. "How marvelous to witness Mother transact the business of the institute!" observed Mother Lombardi. "In struggles she remained tranquil and steady in her confidence in God. She would say, 'We are obliged to do everything possible to defend our cause, which is the Lord's. In the end he will arrange things as he considers best.' But she didn't stand idle. On the contrary, in difficult situations her strength of soul and courage would grow in proportion to the difficulty."

Mother Cabrini was known for her charm and intelligence, and she was as comfortable among wealthy and educated people as she was among the poor and destitute. She had friends who were businessmen and bishops, and friends who were prisoners and poor. Throughout her life, she was attacked by people who resented her vision and leadership, perhaps because she was a woman or because she was Italian—or both. Yet she prevailed, and even through the most unpleasant conflicts, she worked to resolve differences and seek common ground while still achieving her goals.

"In adversity, in misfortune, in unpleasant announcements, I will try to keep my spirit calm, my face serene," she wrote. Sisters who were closest to her commented that she showed her moods very subtly. She would not allow herself to be called the foundress of the Missionary Sisters of the Sacred Heart, for she believed that only Mother Mary herself should be credited for its existence. So when she asked a young Sister to write to the pope in 1916 to wish him a happy new year for her, she was appalled when the Sister signed, "Head of the Institute" beneath Mother Cabrini's name. The Sister was told to tear up the letter and rewrite it without that reference.

How would she want to be remembered? If she could, she would probably insist that instead we remember the four thousand Missionary Sisters of the Sacred Heart for their constant work to alleviate the suffering of poor immigrants. She might want us to remember the six young nuns who left their familiar village in Italy to cross the ocean for the New York City slums in 1889.

Or the Sisters who went from house to house in New Orleans, ministering to the sick and fearful amidst one of the worst outbreaks of yellow fever in history.

Or the Sisters who bravely descended hundreds of feet into a gold mine to speak to men working in harsh, dangerous conditions.

Or the Sisters who sought out Italian prisoners in order to offer comfort, especially to men facing death sentences who had no one who could speak their language.

Or the Sisters who were expelled from their foundations in Panama and Nicaragua under threat of death.

Mother Cabrini would probably have been embarrassed by the majestic ceremony held in Rome on July 7, 1946, where she was canonized by Pope Pius XII in Saint Peter's Basilica. On that day, the bells of Saint Peter's rang out with those of four hundred churches throughout Rome. She was a saint—the first American saint, but surely one most beloved by Italians. It was a magnificent celebration that signified she was now with her namesake, Francis Xavier.

As the *New York Times* reported, religious dignitaries in attendance wore their finest, most colorful clothes for the occasion: "Whitehaired Cardinals in scarlet mingled with bearded patriarchs from the East. Monks of every order and each in his distinctive garb, with chamberlains of cap and sword in early Elizabethan costumes, mace-bearers and penitentiaries, Swiss Guards in their multi-colored uniforms designed by Michaelangelo, Noble Guards in black top boots, white buckskin breeches, red tunics and shining helmets, Palatine guards, mitred Bishops, with choirboys, apostolic couriers with master porters of the Red Rod—the whole formed a riot of color."

Mother Cabrini had been declared venerable in 1937 and the following year, on November 13, 1938, she was beatified based on the stories of two miraculous cures that took place after her death—one in 1921, the other in 1925. November 13 was designated her Feast Day.

The first cure involved a baby boy named Peter Smith who was born at the Columbus Hospital in Chicago in 1921—just three years after Mother Cabrini's death. A nurse inadvertently bathed his eyes with a solution that burned them, causing blindness. He was immediately examined by an eye specialist at the hospital who said that the baby's corneas were gone, and in fact the boy was in danger of dying.

The hospital Superior placed a relic of Mother Cabrini on the boy's gown, and the Sisters prayed for his life throughout the night. The next morning, his temperature had returned to normal and the black scars on his eyes had turned into mild red traces. Within seventy-two hours, Dr. Michael F. Horan and two colleagues declared that the boy's sight had returned to normal. Peter Smith later became a priest.

The second miracle happened in Seattle in 1925. A Missionary Sister named Delfina Grazioli, who had had four operations for gastric cancer, lay dying in the hospital. Doctors told her that the cancer was incurable, and a priest administered extreme unction. Mother Cabrini appeared in a vision to Sister Grazioli, instructing her to eat a hearty meal. A nurse reported this to the Superiors, and asked if she should give Sister Grazioli food—and was told to do so. Soon after eating the meal, Sister Grazoli began to recover. The cancer disappeared, and the nun lived until 1933 to testify to this miracle.

These miracles were accepted by church authorities after the Congregation of Sacred Rites in Rome thoroughly investigated them over a period of ten years. Witnesses, relatives, and followers were brought in to testify, and all their testimonies were recorded and later published.

Many people did not need these miracles to claim Mother Cabrini's status as a saint. She had done much to help the poor all over the world, and knowing quite well that the work was far from over, she inspired generations of women to continue her efforts for years to come.

On the day he made her canonization official, Pope Pius XII said, "May this new saint, may Saint Francesca Xavier Cabrini implore from the Prince of Peace and from the Father of us all that with hates spent, the spirits placated, public, private, and international relations will be regulated not by unbridled desire for selfish advantage, but in justice and equity, restoring to mankind the true peace from which the common good flows. Amen."

About the Author

Nicole is a writer and editor living in Southern California with her husband and son. She has been the home and garden/travel editor at the *Orange County Register*, and has written and edited for numerous publications, including *VIV* magazine, *Family Circle*, *the Boston Globe*, *Los Angeles* magazine, the *Los Angeles Times*, and others. Recent features she's written include stories about a treehouse designer, why we need a surgeon general, how a cocoa bean chemical can reverse memory loss, and reasons to take an inn-to-inn hike along the Southern California coast. When she's not obsessing about her garden, she enjoys traveling, cooking, and reading fiction.

NOW AVAILABLE FROM THE MENTORIS PROJECT

America's Forgotten Founding Father
A Novel Based on the Life of Filippo Mazzei
by Rosanne Welch, PhD

A. P. Giannini—The People's Banker
by Francesca Valente

The Architect Who Changed Our World
A Novel Based on the Life of Andrea Palladio
by Pamela Winfrey

A Boxing Trainer's Journey
A Novel Based on the Life of Angelo Dundee
by Jonathan Brown

Breaking Barriers
A Novel Based on the Life of Laura Bassi
by Jule Selbo

Building Heaven's Ceiling
A Novel Based on the Life of Filippo Brunelleschi
by Joe Cline

Building Wealth
From Shoeshine Boy to Real Estate Magnate
by Robert Barbera

Building Wealth 101
How to Make Your Money Work for You
by Robert Barbera

Christopher Columbus: His Life and Discoveries
by Mario Di Giovanni

Dark Labyrinth
A Novel Based on the Life of Galileo Galilei
by Peter David Myers

Defying Danger
A Novel Based on the Life of Father Matteo Ricci
by Nicole Gregory

The Divine Proportions of Luca Pacioli
A Novel Based on the Life of Luca Pacioli
by W.A.W. Parker

Dreams of Discovery
A Novel Based on the Life of the Explorer John Cabot
by Jule Selbo

The Faithful
A Novel Based on the Life of Giuseppe Verdi
by Collin Mitchell

Fermi's Gifts
A Novel Based on the Life of Enrico Fermi
by Kate Fuglei

First Among Equals
A Novel Based on the Life of Cosimo de' Medici
by Francesco Massaccesi

Grace Notes
A Novel Based on the Life of Henry Mancini
by Stacia Raymond

Harvesting the American Dream
A Novel Based on the Life of Ernest Gallo
by Karen Richardson

Humble Servant of Truth
A Novel Based on the Life of Thomas Aquinas
by Margaret O'Reilly

Leonardo's Secret
A Novel Based on the Life of Leonardo da Vinci
by Peter David Myers

Little by Little We Won
A Novel Based on the Life of Angela Bambace
by Peg A. Lamphier, PhD

The Making of a Prince
A Novel Based on the Life of Niccolò Machiavelli
by Maurizio Marmorstein

A Man of Action Saving Liberty
A Novel Based on the Life of Giuseppe Garibaldi
by Rosanne Welch, PhD

Marconi and His Muses
A Novel Based on the Life of Guglielmo Marconi
by Pamela Winfrey

No Person Above the Law
A Novel Based on the Life of Judge John J. Sirica
by Cynthia Cooper

Relentless Visionary: Alessandro Volta
by Michael Berick

Ride Into the Sun
A Novel Based on the Life of Scipio Africanus
by Patric Verrone

Saving the Republic
A Novel Based on the Life of Marcus Cicero
by Eric D. Martin

Soldier, Diplomat, Archaeologist
A Novel Based on the Bold Life of Louis Palma di Cesnola
by Peg A. Lamphier, PhD

The Soul of a Child
A Novel Based on the Life of Maria Montessori
by Kate Fuglei

What a Woman Can Do
A Novel Based on the Life of Artemisia Gentileschi
by Peg A. Lamphier, PhD

FUTURE TITLES FROM THE MENTORIS PROJECT

A Biography about Rita Levi-Montalcini
and
Novels Based on the Lives of:
Amerigo Vespucci
Andrea Doria
Antonin Scalia
Antonio Meucci
Buzzie Bavasi
Cesare Beccaria
Father Eusebio Francisco Kino
Federico Fellini
Frank Capra
Guido d'Arezzo
Harry Warren
Leonardo Fibonacci
Maria Gaetana Agnesi
Mario Andretti
Peter Rodino
Pietro Belluschi
Saint Augustine of Hippo
Saint Francis of Assisi
Vince Lombardi

For more information on these titles and
the Mentoris Project, please visit
www.mentorisproject.org

Made in the USA
Las Vegas, NV
15 June 2024

91105996R10121